Reader's Digest

Our Nature World Series

Animal Families

Reader's Digest
Our Nature World Series

Animal Families

Glen McBride
Head of the Animal Behavior Unit
University of Queensland, Brisbane, Australia

and the Editors of Reader's Digest

The Reader's Digest Association

Pleasantville, New York   Montreal, Canada   Sydney, Australia

Our Nature World Series
Science Editor

Durward L. Allen
Purdue University

Special Consultants for Animal Families
Hugh Bradford House, *New York Zoological Society*
Olin Sewall Pettingill, Jr., *Cornell University*
Edward R. Ricciuti, *New York Zoological Society*

Contents

What Is a Family?

Without parental care, a raccoon kit or robin nestling
would die. For many animals, the family is a natural sanctuary, a powerful,
protective relationship essential for infant survival

As the time of birth approached, the female wolf entered her den, a tunnel dug into a ridge of sand and gravel. She passed the hollowed-out spot where she usually slept, some seven feet from the entrance, and continued up a slight incline into an enlarged chamber. She sniffed, licked her fur, sprawled out, and waited.

Some hours later, the wolf was awakened by birth contractions. Alternately straining and panting, she expelled her first pup into the world. The tiny, pug-nosed creature struggled against the birth membrane that enveloped it. The mother's licking soon freed the pup's nose and mouth from the sac, then she turned and bit through the umbilical cord attached to its navel.

The pup lurched under the strokes of its mother's tongue. Its thick black fur dried by this rough towel, the pup propped itself up on splayed front feet and whimpered. The bitch wolf nudged her newborn toward the warmth of her body and lay back, breathing heavily.

Over the next three hours, at irregular intervals, five more pups were born. Each in turn was

Alert to danger, a raccoon mother darts to the entrance of the family den, high up in a dead sugar maple. One kit peers out over the packed bodies of its littermates to see what's going on. Litters of two to seven are born in April or May; the mother rears them without help from their father.

groomed, dried, and nudged by its mother. Eyes sealed and unable to hear at birth, the pups were conscious only of the warmth and smells of their mother, the pummeling of her tongue, the taste of milk, and the squirming bodies of littermates. Nursed and comforted, they slept.

Outside, seven other members of the pack lazed in the soft spring weather, two asleep on a grassy ridge above the birthing den. A yearling male, more slightly built than an adult and fuzzier of coat, rolled over on his back at the approach of the pack leader. Tail between his legs, the youngster thrust his snout up to the larger wolf's mouth, and cringed and whined in a continued greeting. Casually the older animal sniffed, stepped over the youngster, and turned away.

Shadows from the tall spruces of the Canadian forest stretched across the rugged terrain, then blurred into evening. The pack assembled and began to howl. From miles away, another wolf chorus answered. Abruptly, in a single file, the wolves set out to hunt. Following the lead male, they trotted briskly for several miles before scenting prey. The growth of trees was too thick for them to see their quarry, but the smell of moose was unmistakable. Each wolf stopped and sniffed, perhaps verifying the direction from which the scent came. Tails wagging, they joined for a brief nose-to-nose ceremony, then fanned out.

Seldom did the wolves encounter so likely a prey so early in the hunt. The moose, old and dis-

Two snarling, biting wolves rolling on the ground may look ferocious, but in all likelihood they are just saying "hello"

eased, fled at the sight of the pack. As he broke into a clearing, the wolves rushed—too soon. The moose bounded forward, eluding them, but in minutes, his strength gone, he turned at bay.

The wolves closed in cautiously. A blow from a hoof could crush a rib or smash a leg. A large male seized the moose by the nose. Beset on all sides, the thousand-pound animal went down. He was quickly killed, and the wolves, who had not eaten in more than five days, gorged themselves.

Stuffed with food, the pack rested that night near the carcass. Toward morning, they set off for the den. The newly delivered mother, hearing their arrival, emerged from the tunnel to greet her packmates. Noses together, tails wagging, the wolves nudged and pushed at each other, furry bodies rolling over in rituals of greeting. The female put her snout up to the leader of the pack as the yearling had done. In a convulsive effort, her mate regurgitated undigested pieces of meat on the ground before the female.

At thirteen days the pups' eyes opened, and they toddled clumsily around in the total darkness of the den, bumping into one another, growling, and chewing on everything they touched. Feeling himself bitten, one pup bit the nearest object, the paw of another pup. Swats and nips were exchanged in the darkness.

The play fights were interrupted as one or another of the pups fell asleep or sought the nipple of its mother. She seldom left the den except to feed. Her incessant licking removed the shedding black fur of infancy. The pups' coats began to assume the mottled gray, brown, white, and black coloration of the adult.

A few days later, now able to hear and see, the pups staggered for the first time out of the den, blinking into the sunlight of a June morning. The members of the pack eagerly crowded around, inspecting the youngsters with sniffs and licks.

The play fighting that began in the den was soon taken up, more avidly than before. Now the opponents could see one another; they were older, stronger, better coordinated.

From time to time, a pup began to explore one of the scents that drifted toward them from the woods, only to be drawn back into the fight by an ambushing littermate. Occasionally, a skirmish was staged over the back of a lounging adult.

Tumbling and nipping in the grass, a month-old male wolf pins a female littermate to the ground. Though still infantile and clumsy, the youngsters establish their rank among themselves at an early age. "Riding up" like this continues to be an important status display in adulthood.

Totally tolerant of the pups, the adult wolf placidly endured their rampaging.

The exuberant, seemingly aimless playing of the pups occasionally turned into real fighting, a contest between two youngsters. "Riding up," paws on the shoulder of a loser, or standing over its prone body, one pup expressed dominance over another. Within a month after birth, the pups had settled among themselves the rank each was to have so long as they remained together.

The return of an adult or yearling wolf from a hunting expedition interrupted the pups' activities. They whined and begged for food, lifting their snouts and pawing the mouth of the returning wolf, as their mother had done to her mate. Their begging was almost always rewarded, for the urge to feed pups is extremely strong in wolves. If the adult had nothing to give, it set out at once to hunt or to dig up a cache of meat.

OVENDEN

When wolf pups are about two months old, the pack abandons the den and begins to wander. The pups are left at a rendezvous site, to which the pack returns after hunting. On arrival, they are greeted by those that stayed behind. A yearling rolls over on its back at the approach of wolves of higher rank. A second wolf, threatened by a dominant male, assumes the ears- and tail-down posture that acknowledges the other's rank. Meanwhile, the pups bound forward, soliciting food from an adult. The wolves rest for a while, then take off again, single file, in search of prey.

Food-begging, which began at four weeks of age, marked the beginning of a gradual weaning from the mother. By eight weeks, the pups received all their food from their elders, who by then were bringing in large pieces of their kills to be chewed and dragged about.

When the pups were about two months old, the pack deserted the den, taking the youngsters with them. After traveling about five miles, the pack settled in a clearing, a "rendezvous" site. Later that night, left alone for the first time since birth as their mother joined the hunt, the pups whimpered a bit, then clumped together to sleep.

Their mother and two other wolves returned at dawn; they had caught nothing. For a week the pack hunted without success, except for small prey—lemmings and snowshoe rabbits. The cubs were introduced to an unpleasant fact of wolf existence—that feast is often followed by famine.

Then at last the wolves killed a moose calf that had strayed too far from its mother's side. The whole pack enjoyed the comfort of a full belly.

By September, the pups were ready to hunt with the pack. Two were lost during their apprenticeship; one was kicked by a moose, and another weakened and died of its burden of parasitic worms. The surviving four took their places in the pack, learning to hunt their food and to behave like adult wolves.

Few animals have a more complex or enduring family life than the wolf. Amiable toward packmates, solicitous of the young, adept at cooperative hunting, their behavior makes survival possible. Other animals, such as monkeys and apes, as well as social insects, live in groups all their lives, but none has so many aspects of behavior that so richly fulfill the notions that humans have when they say "family."

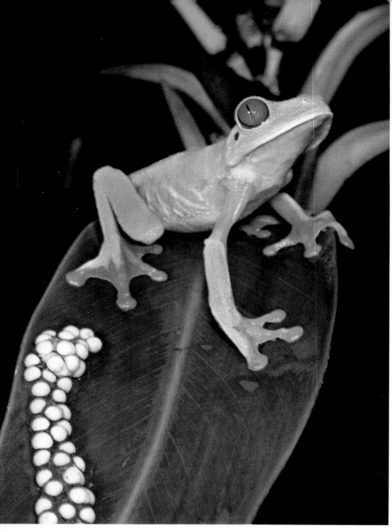

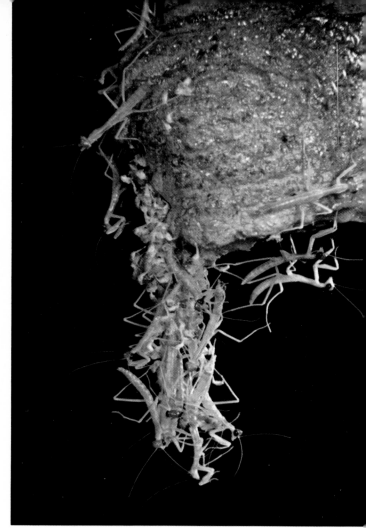

The ruby-eyed tree frog of Central America lays her eggs on a leaf of a bird-of-paradise plant. When it rains, they are washed into a puddle below. Beyond selecting a suitable site for the eggs, the parents give no care at all.

Praying mantids emerge ready for independent life. These mosquito-sized replicas of their parents never see either one. Their mother encases the eggs in a froth and then departs—perhaps having eaten their father during mating.

An alert young bullsnake tears open its leathery shell and slithers out. A native of the plains of North America, the bullsnake is about eighteen inches long at hatching. It fends for itself at once, feeding on rodents and birds.

The No-Family System

In the early ages of animal life on this planet, there were no families as we think of them. There was, it seems, only a broth of microscopic, single-celled animals and plants drifting in the ocean shallows. For the most part, the animals reproduced as amoebas do, by dividing in two, growing to full size again, then redividing, and so on.

Long after these relatively simple forms of life were well established, some organisms developed two sexes. Now male and female were involved in producing offspring. Eggs were laid and fertilized, but the offspring were given no further care. This means of reproduction is still prevalent among most of the animals without backbones, such as insects, shellfish, and worms, and among amphibians and most of the fishes.

Reproduction without care involves massive

overproduction; thousands or even millions of fertilized eggs are left to drift in the seas, or, on land, are deposited on vegetation. The great majority of eggs, as well as hatchlings, are eaten by predators, but enough young survive to carry on the species.

Why Sexes?

The offspring of a sexual union receives half of its characteristics from each parent. The male parent produces sperm—microscopic cells each of which contains half the new individual's hereditary material. The female's eggs, or ova, carry the other half. When the sperm and ovum join, the two halves unite in a single, complete cell, which begins to divide, and a new life starts.

The remarkable thing about sex cells, sperm and ova, is that no two are identical. Sex cells differ from all the other cells in an animal's body because they contain only half the quantity of genetic material—a random selection of all the parent's heritable characteristics. Even simple animals have an enormous number of characteristics, so the number of possible combinations is astronomical. It is as if one scooped out half a pail of sand, identified every grain, then dumped it back, mixed it, and took half again. The likelihood of getting the same grains the next time—or ever—is practically nil.

The variety that is built into sexual reproduction is the vehicle for change in animals, the essence of evolution. In every generation, individual animals vary from their parents and from one another. Each has a unique combination of inherited characteristics.

However, the enduring changes from generation to generation are always slight, almost imperceptible. A pair of ducks will have offspring that seem to be exactly like their parents. Major changes in animals usually take many centuries. The modern horse has existed in its present form for about a million years. The earliest fossil remains of its ancestors show that about 57 million years ago it was not much bigger than a present-day domestic cat.

In this setting of general stability, myriad insignificant changes occur—an ever-so-slightly longer wing, or a new note or new mingling of notes in a bird's song—all products of the genetic roulette that takes place whenever a new individual is formed.

The animals that first concealed their eggs may merely have had a tendency to scratch the soil after laying. Whatever the origin of this behavior,

Reproducing Both Ways

Like many of the lower animals, the tiny freshwater hydra reproduces asexually by "subdividing." But it may also reproduce sexually, ensuring an exchange of characteristics.

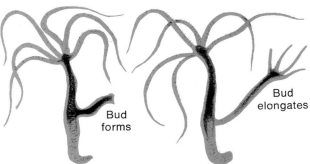

Hydra reproduce asexually by budding. A new individual forms on the trunk of the parent, grows, then breaks off. The offshoot has a genetic makeup identical to its parent.

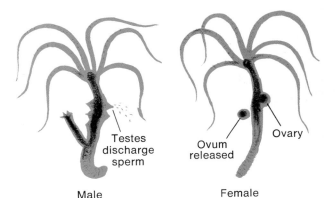

In some species, each individual has a definite sex. The male discharges sperm, the female releases ova. Sexual reproduction allows for a mixing of hereditary materials.

it helped to conceal the offspring and gave them an improved chance for survival. More of the young from hidden eggs would live to adulthood, and pass on to some of their descendants this particular kind of behavior.

The animals of the same kind that did not conceal their eggs would leave fewer offspring because more of their exposed eggs would be eaten by predators. Eventually, many such variations in body form and behavior became established—the heritage of all the animals of a species.

Sometimes the advantageous changes were in an increased ability to hunt, defend, hide, or resist diseases. Every feature of animals that can be seen today is a product of this process of "natural selection." Whether a species of animal has a family life—and the kind of family it has—is also determined by natural selection.

An alligator in the Okefenokee Swamp in Georgia assembles a mound of mud and rubble, deposits her eggs, covers them, then stands guard. Such protection, rare in reptiles, continues even after they hatch, about ten weeks later.

When the female wolf spider's portable egg sac erupts, spilling out 200 or so offspring, she stands still while they climb on board. Her back is a haven for a few days, then the tiny spiders disperse and feed for the first time.

Built-In Behavior

Non-family animals, which receive no care from their parents, must fend for themselves from the moment of hatching. The young spider, insect, or eel finds its own food, evades enemies, and when the time comes, finds a mate and lays or fertilizes eggs, all without assistance. Such animals are born with behavior patterns built-in to meet all their needs. Their development and habits are "programmed" by genetic inheritance. These species put most of their breeding energy into egg production. None is expended on brood-protection or rearing. The female eel lays millions of eggs, but only a few survive to adulthood.

Family-living animals produce fewer young, and the energy is put instead into care of the offspring. The emperor penguin lays but one egg a year, and both parents lavish attention on their single chick. Over the span of their reproductive life, the penguin pair will have about the same batting average as the eel. They will replace themselves in a relatively stable population.

A primitive form of family is found in the Surinam toad, which takes a step toward caring for the young by providing protection for the eggs once they are laid. The male toad fertilizes the eggs of the female, pressing them against her back where they become lodged in wrinkles that form in the skin. For several months she swims and feeds, bulky but unhindered, while the young go through the tadpole stages in her skin. Finally they force their way out as little froglets.

Some nourishment is provided for the young of the mud dauber wasp. The female builds an artificial "eggshell" for her offspring in the form of a mud nest, and installs an artificial "yolk"—an anesthetized caterpillar on which the young can feed at the moment of hatching. After that, the young mud daubers are on their own.

A bit more parental care is given to the newly hatched scorpion. The female carries the young on her back for a few days until their first molt. She provides no food, only safe transportation while they develop. When they have molted, the young drop off and begin independent life. At this point, the female may even eat a few of her young.

The female alligator is one of many animals that exhibit borderline family behavior. Perched on a nest of rotting vegetation, she snaps and hisses at any wild pig, snake, raccoon, or crow that ventures near. As the young alligators struggle free of their shells, they begin croaking. Their mother drags the nest material out of the way, and they wriggle through the rubbish to the surface. Entering the water, the young alligators feed in safety for a while, protected by their mother.

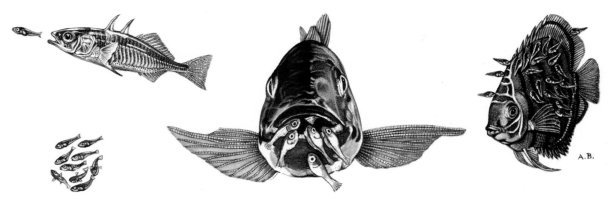

The Special Functions of Fish Parents

Among species of fish that form families, the main benefit to the young is protection from enemies. But adult fish also fan the water around eggs and hatchlings, ensuring that the young receive fresh supplies of oxygen.

A.B.

A stickleback male pursues one of his offspring while the other fry drift above the nest. He retrieves his young for about two weeks.

At the first sign of danger, young tilapia swim into a parent's mouth. In some species, one parent gives care; in other species, both do so.

The first food of discus hatchlings is a mucus secreted from the parents' skin. The young "graze" on both parents for about five weeks.

What Is a Family For?

Many creatures have developed behavior that helps to insulate the new generation from the dangers of the world. The care-giving parent usually defends its young, and it may also provide food, warmth, and a model of adult behavior.

When family life is found in fishes, it is usually confined to protection of the young. The male stickleback, named because of the row of spines along its back, becomes highly colored in the breeding season. He builds a nest, courts a female, and lures her to the nest to lay her eggs, which he then fertilizes. After she leaves, he guards the eggs zealously. When they hatch, he defends the fry, charging at would-be predators. Tirelessly he retrieves the tiny, drifting fry in his mouth and spits them back into the nest.

So vigilant is the stickleback in his parental attentions that when the fry attempt to leave the nest, they must literally escape from him. One by one they reach the surface and gulp a bubble of air. The air is passed to a "swim bladder," a buoyancy chamber within its body. The male stickleback darts after the fry but generally cannot capture any until they come near the nest. Then he snaps them up and spits them back in. This goes on for a few days. Then, as more and more of the young get away and form schools, the male finally

loses interest and swims off, joining a school of other adult sticklebacks.

In some species of tilapia, a freshwater fish of Africa and Asia Minor, the female retains the eggs in her mouth until hatching. For about five days thereafter, the young take shelter in their mother's mouth whenever danger threatens. To feed, the female spits the eggs or fry out, catches and eats her prey, then gathers them back into her mouth again.

Direct feeding of young is extremely rare in fishes. The discus fish of the Amazon basin is one of these exceptional species. Both male and female secrete a nutritious mucus on their sides. The fry graze on one parent while the other is away. Changing of the guard is accomplished promptly. The "nursing" parent spurts away on the approach of its mate, too swiftly for the fry to follow. They resume feeding on the sides of the second parent.

Family behavior is highly specialized in certain insects. Care of the offspring is an essential part of the lives of termites, ants, and social bees and wasps. Eggs and larvae are safely housed in hives, hills, or underground chambers. Adult workers—sterile females—feed the young. The adults even provide environmental control by maintaining humidity and air circulation in their nests.

Barren-ground caribou calves are born into a forbidding environment, sometimes with snow still on the ground. Those born in daytime survive even these rugged conditions. Birth at night is more hazardous, for the young may be iced over.

Warm-blooded animals overthrew the dominance of reptiles. The key to success was in the evolution of family life

For millions of years, the Earth was inhabited only by cold-blooded animals such as insects, amphibians, and reptiles. These creatures rely on the sun to provide the heat they need for activity; they become sluggish when the temperature drops.

The cold-blooded animals prospered throughout the world when days were hot and nights generally moderate. But when the Earth's climate changed, and cold weather dominated parts of the globe, the activities of cold-blooded creatures were greatly restricted. A cool spring or autumn evening immobilized them, and throughout the long winters, nothing stirred.

Competition for food and space led animals to invade every habitat on Earth that could support life. Until some creatures could take advantage of cold conditions, the night and the winter remained open to colonization.

Through countless accumulating adaptations, two groups of animals, the birds and mammals, evolved the ability to generate body heat and maintain their internal temperatures even when the surrounding temperatures dropped. Such animals, the warm-blooded creatures, also evolved insulation of various kinds—feathers, fur, layers of fat—to conserve heat. And they gained the capacity to throw off excessive heat when the temperatures rise by sweating, panting, and otherwise ventilating their bodies. The earliest primitive mammals, which appeared in the time of the dinosaurs, probably adapted first to the cool nights. They could attack the sluggish reptiles, perhaps much larger than themselves, and feed on their eggs. Over vast stretches of time, they ventured to colonize the winter. The early small mammals were highly successful; they diversified and came to inhabit the whole Earth.

Though capable of activity throughout day and night and in all seasons, many warm-blooded animals avoid extremes of temperature when they can. In the heat of an African noonday sun, lions prefer to nap. But a lion can and will hunt in the scorching heat, if pressed by hunger.

The Significance of Size

If an elephant were to be put in one box and sixty-four jaguars into another of the same size, the same amount of paint would be needed to cover each box. But if the cats were boxed separately, four times as much paint would be needed.

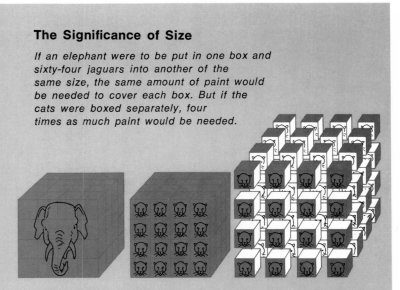

The elephant and the jaguars illustrate the point that the ratio of surface (skin) to volume (body) varies directly, depending on how big an animal is. Body heat is lost through the skin, and so this ratio is important. Small animals, with proportionally more surface to volume, must eat a great deal to replace lost heat. This explains in part why a relatively large caribou calf can endure cold, and a litter of weasels needs a nest.

A litter of weasels *mills around in their underground nest, which their mother lined with fur from a cottontail rabbit. Thus the helpless infants are kept warm until their own fur grows.*

Warmth for Warm-Blooded Young

The constant body temperature of birds and mammals, with all its advantages, also involves a liability. From the moment of conception to hatching or birth, the developing embryo needs heat that it cannot provide for itself. The female mammal keeps the fetus warm by carrying it within her own body. Pregnancy seldom impedes her freedom of movement.

Internal growth of the embryo would not be practical for birds—the additional weight would hinder flight. Birds retained the egg-laying behavior of their reptilian ancestors, but like mammals, birds evolved a way to provide warmth for the embryo from the adult's body, by incubating eggs. The evolution of hard shells protected delicate embryos from being crushed by the motion of the parent bird.

Most birds also build nests that retain heat, thus allowing the parent to leave the eggs for short periods. Some birds build in cavities, others line their nests with down, and still others cover their nests when they leave them.

Almost every species of bird forms a family. One or both parents defend the brood from enemies, bring them food or lead them to feeding grounds, and regularly settle over the youngsters to warm them. The length of time young birds are in a family, and the degree of care they receive, vary widely. Only one group of birds, the megapodes of Australia and Indonesia, have chicks that are fully independent at hatching.

There are no mammals that do not form families. The mother always provides care and protection for a time, because her milk is essential to the newborn. Hoofed animals such as deer and antelope give birth to well-developed young that are able to stand and nurse within a few minutes. For them, food is more important than warmth.

Small mammals generally give birth to offspring at an earlier stage of development. Newborn skunks, for example, are blind, naked, and helpless. The mother often expends a great deal of energy building a nest in preparation for their birth. The nest may be underground, in a burrow, or in long grass out of the wind. Mammalian young may draw warmth from their mothers by snuggling close to sleep against her flank. Cats and mink and many other mothers assist by curving their bodies into a sheltering arc.

The mallee fowl of Australia has perhaps the most elaborate incubation system of all birds. In late fall, the male digs a pit about three feet deep, fifteen feet wide, into which he scrapes plant litter. Midwinter, he covers the heap with sand. The sealed-in vegetation ferments, giving off heat. The female begins laying eggs in early spring; at irregular intervals for almost seven months, she lays as many as thirty-five eggs. Meanwhile, the male constantly tests and adjusts the temperature of the "incubator."

A male frequently plunges his beak into the mound to test temperature. Apparently his tongue is his "thermometer."

Each time she lays an egg, a female tests the mound. If it is not at about 92° F., she waits till the male adjusts it.

More sand raises temperature

Less sand cools nest

The sun and the decay of vegetation provide heat. The sand acts as an insulator, and is added or scraped off.

The young hatch at about seven weeks, each chick climbing out by itself. It needs no further care from its parents.

All mammals and almost all species of birds receive some kind of parental care in early infancy

A newly hatched bird or newborn mammal may not be independent; nevertheless, it is fully equipped for the first stage of life. Its earliest responses are not to the world around, but to its parent. A nestling bird gapes to its parent for food; a young squirrel immediately seeks its mother's teat. The young animal enters the limited world of the nest or burrow, or possibly is confined by its mother's tendency to retrieve it when it wanders. The parent is a buffer from enemies and the elements. As long as the youngster directs its attentions toward the adult, it will have comparative security.

All animals are born with a set of instinctive patterns that enable them to establish a toehold in life. In contrast to tadpoles and lizards, which have inherited the ability to fend for themselves from the moment of hatching, dependent young have inherited a tendency to rely on adults. Many of the self-protective forms of behavior common to non-family animals are absent. A tadpole can flee a predator; a monkey infant cannot. Family young seek their parent, and the parent "reinforces" this activity with its responses. When the doe licks her fawn, she is also focusing its attention on herself.

Shielded in the critical period of its infancy from making a fatal mistake, the young family animal has an opportunity to learn through trial and error. The advantage is that it has greater flexibility in what it is ultimately able to do. The female lion or tiger shows her young a variety of hunting techniques. A young chimpanzee learns what its mother is eating, and how to collect food. Its mother prevents it from eating items that may be harmful.

Whenever danger threatens, the infant animal sees what alarmed its mother and also experiences fear. Thus it learns what danger is and ways in which the troop responds to it. All the adults contribute to its education.

Generally, the longer the period of dependency, the more the animal learns. Guinea pigs, which are born fully furred, eyes open, and able to run within a few hours, live in a family for only three weeks before going off on their own. Their learn-

A koala mother rears her offspring alone—and for quite a long time. The infant migrates from womb to pouch at one month (koalas are not bears but relatives of opossums); it remains inside for six months, then rides piggyback for six.

In one of the rare instances of role reversal among birds, the male painted snipe cares for the young all by himself. Not only is the female more brightly plumed, but she initiates courting, and provides eggs for several males.

ing is of a meager sort. A wolf pup, on the other hand, is dependent for many months, and in fact is seldom solitary even as an adult. The pup is clumsy at first in everything it does; it may even have trouble finding a teat after birth. But in time it becomes proficient in a wide range of activities, from group defense to cooperative hunting of large prey.

One-Parent Families

Single-parent families abound in the animal kingdom. The social insects—bees, wasps, and ants—live in communities dominated by one or several females. The role of the male honeybee is brief; once he fertilizes the queen, he usually dies. Thereafter, all the activities of this matriarchal society are concerned with the care of the queen and her eggs, food-sharing, and defense.

Most mammals have single-parent families. The role of the female is obligatory; only she is capable of producing milk on which the young depend. Often the female is entirely solitary when rearing young, associating neither with her mate nor with others of her species. The tigress or wild pig sow needs no assistance in protecting her offspring; few animals would venture near such a fierce adversary.

Smaller, less formidable females—deer mice, voles, chipmunks—also rear their young alone. These creatures are food for many predators, so their life is one of endless caution. They hide their young in burrows or holes in trees. The doe rabbit carefully arranges tufts of grass at the entrance of the nest whenever she leaves it.

Though hoofed animals frequently live in herds, the family unit is usually the mother and offspring. Membership in a large group confers some protection, but as a rule the only sure defender of a threatened calf or fawn is its mother. She alone will search until a lost youngster is found.

Within the social structure of a monkey troop, the infants with their mothers form many individual families under the protection of the strongest males. The role of the infant's father is general; he does not single out his own offspring for particular care.

A bird's appearance sometimes reveals its parental role. If the male's plumage is brilliantly colored and the female's is inconspicuous, the likelihood is that the male lives a bachelor's life and that the female rears the young.

Male birds of paradise, most flamboyant of all birds, give no care to their offspring. Nor does the showy jungle fowl cock, resplendent in black, red, and gold plumage, or the magnificently plumed sage grouse male. The drab, inconspicuous females of these species take on the whole job of nest-building, incubation, and protection of chicks while they feed in the long grass.

Though such a mother rears her young alone, this does not always mean that she receives no assistance from the male. Several females with their broods live in the area claimed by a male jungle fowl. The alarm call of the vigilant male is normally their first warning of the approach of a predator.

In a few exceptional species, it is the male that does the job of rearing. From the time the eggs are laid, the male rhea takes full charge of nesting and rearing the young. This ostrich-like bird of the South American pampas courts several females. Each lays her eggs in the nest he has built in the waving grasses. With much fluffing of feathers and extreme care, he settles his broad, fifty-pound body on the eggs or chicks. He meets any intruder with a warning hiss, followed up by violent blows with his bill if the first warning is not heeded. The rhea cares for his charges for about six weeks, leading them over his range, feeding with them, and regularly settling over the striped chicks to warm them.

Male and female birds often share parental duties, for the young are soon on the scene. Not so for mammals

Though most chicks that are led to food are generally cared for by a single parent, there are exceptions. Most species of geese form pairs, guarding their flotilla of goslings front and back as the young feed on a lake.

Among songbirds, birds of prey, and shorebirds, both parents cooperate in feeding their young. After hatching, a tern chick stays at the nest, and both parents bring back fish from the sea. The advantage is that the young have continuous protection as the parents take turns at the nest.

Parental sharing of feeding duties also provides the young with more food in a shorter period of time, with the likely result that they will grow more quickly and leave the nest sooner. Once the young fledge, they are less vulnerable to enemies.

Though the male cardinal brings food to his mate and offspring, he spends little time on the nest incubating or brooding. His plumage is a vivid, eye-catching red, in contrast with the drab olive brown of the female. Nesting tasks fall to the female, who is less conspicuous to marauders.

Commonly, where the plumage and appearance of male and female are identical, the male shares incubation with the female more equally. In a smooth, well-integrated operation, a pair of North African spur-winged plovers take turns sitting, one relieving the other throughout the day. Together they lead their speckled chicks to the edge of a marsh or creek, where all feed together for a few days.

Then the plover parents separate—but not far apart—and each takes roughly half the number of chicks, to brood, guard, and lead to food. A passing human being will bring two furious parents swooping down with harsh cries. Responding to the parents' alarm calls, the chicks lie flat and almost invisible in the grass.

There are few pair-forming species among mammals. The gibbon—a furry, long-limbed ape of Southeast Asia—the wolf, badger, chinchilla, and red fox are among the few mammals that do. The beaver is a pair-former, perhaps because cooperation is necessary to build a dam, lodge, and canals. Usually the young beaver is ejected from its home lodge at the age of two years. It becomes clear that the youngster is no longer welcome around the pond, and it goes off to begin life as an adult. In a short time, a young male is joined by a female of about the same age who has been evicted from her family.

Together the pair of beavers set about keeping the dam in order, enlarging their lodge, digging canals, and, in the fall, building food caches. When kits are born in the spring, both parents shepherd them protectively whenever they venture out of the lodge. The following year, when there is a second litter, the yearlings are tolerated. But in another summer, they are compelled to leave the colony and begin independent life at some distance from home.

Beavers are often paired for many seasons, possibly for life. This may be because the lodge is so constructed that it can easily last a beaver lifetime, which would tend to stabilize relationships between paired males and females.

Red foxes pair each year in the breeding season, remaining together until the young are reared. A male may mate with the same female the following year, but not invariably.

The jackal father cooperates with the mother in rearing the young. Paternal care is unusual in mammals, occurring mainly in members of the dog family. Like wolves and foxes, the male jackal helps his mate feed and guard their pups.

A buzzard parent alights with a snake in its beak for the nestlings. Like most birds of prey, male and female buzzard share parental chores—though the mother usually has the task of shredding the prey and distributing the pieces.

Diving for the kill, a young red-tailed hawk is put off its aim by the sudden, effective defense of a mother opossum. Her half-grown youngsters clutch at her fur, prepared to hang on when she scurries away from the field of combat.

The Vital Services of Parents

Many birds are meticulous housekeepers. They begin their chores by removing shells. The young usually defecate soon after feeding, and the parent picks up the fecal sac and carries it away.

The universal function of parents is the protection of young. Some hide their offspring, others will stand between their young and a marauding enemy. Many birds and all mammals also provide food. Depending on species, the parent may shield its youngsters from the cold—birds by sitting on the nest, mammals by constructing nests in the ground or curling their bodies around their young, transferring their own body heat to helpless infants. The mammal mother that licks her youngster's fur keeps the coat in good condition, as do bird parents that preen the nestlings' feathers. Some infants are even given instruction of sorts—a model of adult behavior to copy.

A newborn caracal pokes its head up as its mother licks it dry. Like all cats, caracals are utterly dependent at birth. Concealed in a thicket, the mother nurses her two infants, and cradles them against the cool of a Kenya evening.

A little blue heron parent is besieged by nestlings that almost fall out of the nest in their eagerness. At first, both parents disgorge food into the nest. Within a week, a nestling tugs on its parent's beak and feeds directly.

Raccoon kits watch intently as their mother lifts a flat rock in search of crayfish. The youngsters imitate her every move, but they are overeager and clumsy. There must be many such "lessons" before the kits become efficient hunters.

Each species of animal forms family ties only under certain conditions. If there is any disruption, the vital link may not be forged

When a child falls from a playground swing and lets out a howl, his mother hurries to the rescue. This is such an ordinary occurrence that nobody questions it. Animal mothers react in the same way. A cry of distress from a polar bear cub brings 700 pounds of maternal concern on the run.

It is only when something goes wrong—when a human mother abandons her children, or when a mother cat inexplicably rejects her kittens—that it becomes clear how strong and automatic is the normal mother-offspring relationship. This form of attachment is essential to the very survival of the species.

The strong feeling that humans call "love" holds human families together—though not always. When a pair of robins sets up housekeeping in the backyard, dutifully attending to each other and to their offspring, it is tempting to say that there is an animal kind of love, too. There may be, but there is no evidence that animals experience anything as complex as the feelings that people associate with the word "love." Recognizing this, scientists have settled on the word "bond" to describe the attachment that some animals have for one another.

Bonds are the glue that holds families together, whether a parent with its young or a male and female in a "pair bond." Littermates may also form bonds with one another. Animals with these strong attachments behave differently toward one another than they do toward other members of their species. A gull may freely approach its own mate or chicks, but is fiercely attacked if it approaches the nest of another gull.

A Time of Isolation

In a dense thicket, away from the pride to which she belongs, a lioness gives birth to her cubs. For eight weeks she devotes full attention to them. Then, leading her wobbly offspring back to the pride, she introduces them to a different life —a world populated with as many as a score of other lions of all ages. During their period of seclusion, strong ties were formed between the mother lion and her litter, so that, though they associate with others in the pride, they are primarily attached to her and to one another. Their mother is not just a source of food for the cubs. Like most young mammals, lion youngsters seek their mother's company at intervals throughout the day—almost as if they are "touching base."

This period of isolation, during which bonds may be formed most efficiently, commonly occurs among mammals that live in groups. The period may be brief and the distance of separation slight in some herd animals. Members of the deer family have relatively long periods of isolation. Monkeys are exceptional; the mother moves to the center of the troop before the infant is born and remains there for quite a while afterward.

Recognition

Each species of animal has its own way of recognizing the individuals to which it is bonded— whether mate or offspring. When elephant seals gather in their crowded rookeries, pups are left to wander while their mothers are off feeding. On returning, a cow elephant seal calls loudly as she wades into the bedlam of roaring, heaving animals. Many seal pups approach her, crying urgently to nurse. But usually she will respond only to her own.

Mammals are mainly dependent on scent for recognition. Each individual has a distinctive odor; the mother learns to identify the scent of her offspring at birth, and the young that of the mother. Young buffalo calves playing together are easily sorted out by their mothers. As the young animal grows older, cow and calf evidently are able to pick one another out of the crowd by their appearance as well.

Birds rely primarily on sound, though sight recognition is common. The Bewick swan, for example, has a distinctively marked beak that others of their kind can identify. Few birds have a sense of smell—the kiwi of New Zealand is one of these rarities, but smell is used to hunt for worms at night, not for recognizing one another.

Recognition is truly remarkable in the vast rookeries of birds, where to all appearances the males and females are identical, and nestlings seem to have no distinguishing marks.

An Adélie penguin parent, returning from the sea with a gullet full of food, begins calling as it comes up the beach. It heads for the site of the nest—which has been reduced to a mass of scattered pebbles. The young, recognizing their parent's voice, leave the "crèche" where they have

Only six minutes old, still damp from birth, a white-tailed deer fawn begins to nurse. The mother licks it dry, but does not remain with her offspring for long. The scentless youngster is safest alone; the white spots of its coat blend with the sun-dappled forest floor, camouflaging it from predators. The mother is attentive—but at a distance.

gathered with other chicks and rush to the nest site to be fed. Other chicks sometimes tag along but, for the most part, the penguin parent feeds only its own. The parent recognizes the voices of its chicks—but arrival at an established family site also seems to help the adult to distinguish its own from other young beggars.

Both elephant seals and Adélie penguins sometimes relax the rule of exclusive care if their own offspring are dead or lost, and may feed an orphan or an especially importunate youngster.

But usually recognition is a matter of life and death. Sheep, which recognize their young by scent, will not adopt an orphan, even if their own offspring has died. To stimulate the ewe's maternal behavior and arrange for an adoption, sheepherders used to cut the skin from a dead lamb and tie it over an orphan. Now the method is to

spray both the ewe and orphan with the same scent, to form the basis for a bond. It is a measure of the force of scent-recognition among sheep that this deception works.

Many small rodents such as rats "recognize" their young just because they are in the nest. It is possible, when the mother is absent, to add strays to the litter — or to subtract residents — without disturbing her or in any way altering her maternal behavior. She cares for the newcomers as though they were her own, and does not search for missing infants.

The nest is likewise the basis for bonding in many birds. Adults of some species will care for whatever young they find in their nest. Night heron nestlings do not recognize their parents as individuals. Only the parents visit the nest, performing a nest-approach ceremony on arrival, a stately bowing of the head. Once, a scientist so disturbed a returning parent night heron that it failed to perform this ceremony, whereupon it was attacked by its own nestlings.

When a marmot's nest is disturbed, the mother totes her infants to a new one. Each time this mother emerged from the old den, she sat at the entrance, looking for enemies. Then she sprinted off with an infant in her mouth.

Keeping in Touch

Straying from the nest, a helpless newborn mouse or mink soon misses its familiar surroundings and whimpers or cries. The attentive mother hears and quickly carries or nudges it back to the nest. Retrieval of the young is found in all family animals, and is vital to their survival. A lost youngster is in grave peril, for without a mother it has no defenses against any predator.

When the mother leads her young away from a nest, the problem of keeping together becomes more difficult; a moving mother is easily lost by a momentarily inattentive infant. Traveling through dense vegetation, animals frequently communicate by sound, emitting squeaks, twitters, or chirps. A sow pig grunts at regular intervals, letting the piglets know where she is; they keep in contact with her and each other by similar grunts.

When a grouse chick loses contact with its mother, it gives a special distress call. The grouse mother responds by collecting her other chicks; then, in convoy, she seeks the lost one. Even at a distance, she recognizes the call of her young.

Bonded pairs of adults also keep in touch with one another. Two house sparrows chirp and flip their tails whenever they land. They constantly announce their locations as they hunt separately for food. Whenever a human being walks through the woods, much of what he hears — and sometimes sees — is concerned with an animal's saying, "I am here."

A night heron signals peaceful intentions by bowing, which shows off its glossy bluish-black cap and raises the three slender white plumes at the back of its head. This nest-approach ceremony allows it to enter its nest unchallenged.

Bonds Are Built by Behavior

Bonds do not just happen; they are always the result of the way animals behave toward one another. The building of a bond through courtship is the prelude to mating among family-forming birds. Every year when the common terns arrive for the breeding season on the east coast of North America, there is great commotion in the nesting colonies. The process of mate-selection is complicated by the fact that male and female terns are identical in plumage.

Courtship begins when a male common tern catches a small fish in his beak and, with wings outstretched, offers it to a tern approaching overhead. If the new arrival is a male, he postures in the same way, which prompts the first male to drive him off. The general excitation in the colony is heightened by many such encounters.

If, however, the arrival is a female tern, she adopts a begging posture with wings closed, and the male passes the fish to her. When she takes it the male immediately begs for it back. The fish is not eaten, but is passed back and forth several times between the courting birds. As the ceremony is repeated, the mates become used to one another, and a bond develops between them. Together they go about the business of nest-building, mating, and later, incubation of the eggs and feeding and protection of the chicks.

Sometimes courtship gestures take the form of preening the opposite sex. A bird draws feathers of the other through its beak, appearing to clean them. This nibbling at feathers, which birds do for themselves continually, seems to produce pleasurable sensations. Some of the preening and rubbing looks much like a caress. Budgerigars, often called lovebirds, court by perching side by side and preening one another.

A male gannet sits on its nest to invite female attention, bowing slightly and holding his wings at his side. When a female approaches, he attempts to seize her by the nape of the neck. If she is receptive, she cooperates and presents her neck by turning her head away. The pair then face each other and fence with their bills, either clacking them together in a kind of swordplay, or in a

Bonding Begins with a Formal Announcement

Each of the pair-forming species of birds has a particular ritual to initiate courtship. The gesture or activity is often derived from some other function, as when a male roseate spoonbill offers nesting material to a prospective mate. It is much too soon for nest-building, nevertheless the gesture serves to open the *proceedings. A male black and white warbler woos a female by chasing her through the air. Just before mating, the male kingfisher presents the female with a fish. Ceremonies such as these, perhaps abbreviated or taking an entirely different form, are performed for as long as the pair remains together.*

Roseate spoonbill   Black and white warbler   Kingfisher

The courtship of wandering albatrosses includes rattling, vibrating, and touching bills. The display reaches its highest intensity when each bird spreads its wngs—an amazing eleven-foot span from tip to tip. The males arrive first at breeding grounds in the South Atlantic. When a female lands, several males display, then she chooses a mate.

whetting motion where the bills are repeatedly rubbed against one another.

In almost every case, a call, song, honking, or trumpeting accompanies the courtship gestures of birds. These rituals become abbreviated with time, but continue for as long as the pair stays together. In this way the bond is maintained—expressed and reaffirmed.

The duration of the bond varies greatly from one bird species to another. The male ruffed grouse has an elaborate courtship ritual involving both drumming on a log and plumage display. If this captures the female's attention, the pair quickly mate, then go their separate ways. Though there has been courtship, it has been only the briefest of encounters, and does not result in a lasting bond. The male then courts other females.

Some small songbirds rear more than one set of young and so stay together for the spring, the summer, and into the autumn. The house wren, for example, often raises two broods. As part of the courtship ritual, the male wren builds several nests, of which his mate will choose one. When the female begins laying her second clutch of eggs, the male leads the older brood to roost in one of the surplus nests.

In seasons or regions that have a rich supply of food, the male wren may have more than one mate in his domain. In this case, he becomes strongly bonded to all his mates, and to the offspring in each nest. In fact, if a female wren deserts her nest, the male will almost invariably take over care of the young.

The length of time the paired birds remain

Hungry bystanders watch *as an emperor penguin feeds its fifteen-week-old chick. Both parents work full time to keep up with the appetite of their single offspring. They sort out their own youngster by its voice. The chick, too, recognizes its parents' calls. When a parent arrives, the chick waddles toward it, guided by sound; others often tag along.*

together in breeding season is closely tied to the needs of the young. Usually, the bond holds until the juveniles fledge and are able to fend for themselves. Then adults and youngsters generally fly off to join a winter flock.

Enduring Ties

Some pair bonds are remarkable for their permanence; several species are monogamous for life. Swans, geese, and jackdaws form such enduring ties. Many seabird pairs remain together during nesting, separate until the next breeding season, then return to the same nest site and pair with their mate of the previous year.

Most mammals do not form bonds with their mates. The small burrowers come together fleetingly to mate; the larger mammals, in which the females may be rounded up by the male in a harem for several days, weeks, or months, do not seem to form strong attachments.

The association of male and female mammals usually ends long before the young are born. Therefore the male has no bond with his offspring. The female's bond with her young is formed at birth when she licks the newborn dry and nurses it, which guarantees that the infant and its mother learn one another's scent.

For some nest-building mammals, the bond seems to be based on the scents in the nest, and departure of the litter from the nest terminates the bond. Others continue family care away from the nest. By this time, parents and offspring recognize one another individually, by scent, sound, and eventually by sight.

A pack of wolves crowds around a dominant male—leader of the pack—in a "group ceremony" of greeting. Pushing and jostling to get close, they express their submission by licking his face and gently biting his muzzle. The ritual is performed whenever a wolf returns after a brief absence, and is a means of reinforcing social relationships.

Social Bonds

The pair bond, where present, and the parent-offspring bond are the strongest known. However, any close association of individual animals within societies results in clearly established relationships, or social bonds. In the wolf pack each animal expresses by its behavior what its role is in the group. The leader is given deference by the yearlings and all other adults; one female has higher rank than others, and she receives similar gestures that signify her high status.

Within the wolf pack, the dominant male and female form a pair bond at the time of mating; usually they alone breed. The parents also form bonds with their young. These bonds change as the mating season passes and as the pups mature. Throughout the year, the social bonds are constantly expressed by play or greetings.

The bond within which a wolf pup was nurtured gives way to the cooperative bond of hunters as the yearling joins its sire on the chase. Eventually yearling and full-grown offspring, both male and female, nurture their mother by bringing home food for her and for the new litter.

A troop of monkeys is also held together by strong social bonds. Their society is generally larger than the wolf pack, and the dominance system more variable. All mature females breed; their status becomes higher when they are in breeding condition and when the young are born. Groups of females, especially mothers and daughters, associate constantly. Other relationships develop in play, in countless hours spent grooming each other, and perhaps passively, as animals feed and rest in each other's company.

Though the endless, careful picking at fur and the antics of juveniles seem trifling, they have the effect of welding the group into a close-knit unit. At the approach of an intruder, all are instantly ready for coordinated defense or flight.

All-female herds of water buffalo and flocks of wild sheep have loose social bonds. Mothers and adult daughters, each with her latest offspring, graze together, often led by the eldest female. These females, however, do not seem to express their relationships with one another as formally or as frequently as do the members of wolf and monkey societies.

A male baboon grooms the fur of a female, carefully parting the fur and removing particles of dead skin, insects, and other foreign matter. This is obviously pleasurable, and serves not only to keep the fur in good condition but to establish bonds between individuals. A dominant male receives the most grooming, but all enjoy some attention.

A "pod" of about 2000 *recently weaned elephant seal pups congregates on the beach of San Miguel Island, off the coast of California. Well supplied with fat, and sharing the* *general warmth of so many bodies nearby, they lie like lazy Sunday beachgoers for three months. Then, driven by hunger, they launch themselves into the sea to feed.*

Signs of Change

As the breeding season draws to a close, a marked indifference develops between paired birds of most species. When their offspring become independent, pairs do not stay together, or indeed with the juveniles.

As the temperature, daylength, and availability of food change, animals change too. Within the body of the parent, there is a reversing or withdrawal of the hormonal influences that caused it to bond, mate, and rear young. And the young outgrow the appearance and behavior that stimulated parental care.

The first sign of breakup in paired birds is a decrease in the bonding activities that welded them together. The male common tern may not bring a gift of fish to his mate as often as before. The female gannet may fail to turn her neck when the male attempts to catch her with his bill. As the young approach independence, one or both parents leave the brood on their own to a greater

extent, perhaps actively avoiding the offspring. As the bonds begin to weaken, each slighted task or outright rejection leads to avoidance.

Nowhere is the breakup of the bond more dramatic than in the withdrawal of parents from their young. This takes place gradually as the developing animal approaches independence. But the juveniles often resist their parents' withdrawal. Long after they are able to fend for themselves, fledgling gulls may be seen begging food from their parents—who, indeed, sometimes give in. But this occurs less and less often, and eventually, merely approaching a parent will earn the young bird a sharp peck or threat.

Even after they are able to live entirely on adult food, young mammals pester their mother to be allowed to nurse. The mother's supply of milk declines rapidly when the growing youngsters' appetites approach adult proportions.

A female tiger introduces her cubs to meat at six to twelve weeks of age. If the distance to the kill is short, she will either bring her cubs to it or will drag the food to the den. If she has killed prey far from the den, the tigress will gorge herself and then, on returning, will regurgitate partly digested meat for the cubs.

The tigress begins the weaning process by making herself less and less available for nursing. She bares her fangs and hisses at the cubs, thus keeping them away. At first the cubs persist, but in a short time, after a few angry swats, they get the message.

Young langur monkeys of India also put up a fight to retain their mother's company at night. They may throw temper tantrums and make repeated attempts to join her at dusk. Her rejection continues. Eventually they are forced to sleep apart from her at night, usually forming clusters with other rejected youngsters.

A Falling-Out

This is a trying time in the life of a young animal, frequently more so for males than for females. In troops of monkeys and apes, for example, the young female may be prevented from nursing, but after the initial period of weaning, when she is driven away from her mother, she is soon allowed to rejoin her. In this way a small group of females—daughters and granddaughters—builds up around older females.

The return of the juvenile female to her mother's family is made easier by her tendency to groom adult females and infants. She is able to maintain these friendly relationships during the period of rejection by her mother. She grows to maturity surrounded by females, and in turn becomes a mother.

Juvenile male monkeys, on the other hand, have rowdier tendencies and are regularly disciplined by adults for their disorderly behavior. They spend most of their time in rough-and-tumble play, wrestling and chasing after others in their age group. They are too rambunctious to be trusted with infants.

The result is that young males in a monkey family tend to be rejected first, and the breaking of their bond with their mother is more or less complete. Their fate varies from species to species. Adolescent olive baboons and Japanese monkeys remain within the troop, associating mainly with other subordinate males. Gelada baboons are driven out of the harem group as soon as they reach sexual maturity; they join bands of young males and remain somewhat separate until they are able to form a harem.

Just out of the nest, a young Puerto Rican emerald hummingbird begs its parent for food. At this point, some parents lose interest and a fledgling must fend for itself.

Weaning Means Rejection

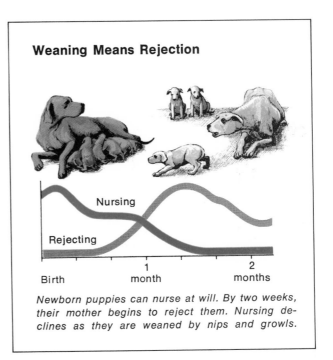

Nursing

Rejecting

Birth | 1 month | 2 months

Newborn puppies can nurse at will. By two weeks, their mother begins to reject them. Nursing declines as they are weaned by nips and growls.

A female grizzly bear rushes to rescue her cub, under attack by a cougar. The terrified cub, which had wandered

too far from its mother, is no match for the lightning-swift cat, and lets out a cry as the cougar overtakes it. The en-

Under normal conditions, the parent-offspring bond is not broken until the young are able to fend for themselves

The importance of the family bond becomes clear when, through the death or dereliction of a parent, the relationship is broken prematurely. A tiger cub that has been abandoned by its mother will certainly starve to death, or fall prey to a jackal or other roving enemy that would never try to attack when its mother was nearby. Even though a bear cub may have been weaned, it is usually not able to survive the premature loss of its mother. It is not a good hunter or forager at an early age, and probably could not eat enough to build its strength for survival through the

winter. Unprotected, the bear cub is easy prey for a cougar. But bonds are normally broken only when the young are ready for independent life.

Premature loss of parental protection is usually due to the death of a parent, but sometimes it is because the parent is deficient in behavior. The parent may fail to act as others of its species do at a particular time. If a male bird flits off leaving his mate to incubate and care for the young alone, the nestlings' unappeased hunger may make them more restless and noisier in the nest than if both parents were bringing food. Their constant cries may attract a cat. The female's efforts to distract the marauder—fluttering to the ground, dragging an apparently broken wing—may fail. Flying at the cat directly, as her mate might have done, may also fail. The young may well be carried off to feed a litter of kittens, or the nestlings of a hawk or other bird of prey.

The restlessness of the young has the same di-

raged grizzly faces the cat. It's a standoff, for the cougar cannot fight the mother and still catch the cub. Secure *under its mother's protection, the cub watches as the thwarted cat spits defiantly, and finally gives up.*

sastrous result whether their father's loss was due to death or dereliction. And normally reared broods are also frequently killed. But if the male continues to neglect his offspring in succeeding matings, the young would always be more vulnerable to predators. During his life, such a bird would be likely to leave few offspring. Thus natural selection blocks the passing on of undesirable heritable characteristics.

The value of the bond in ensuring the survival of new generations cannot be overestimated. Evolved over millions of years, this behavioral tie has extraordinary power. A parent will readily jeopardize its own life for its offspring.

On an expedition to Ellesmere Island in northern Canada, two scientists kidnapped two wolf pups out of a litter of four by chasing off their guardian, a male wolf, in an exhausting, mile-long run. On their way back to the base camp, they shot some ptarmigan. Laden with an armful

of wolf pup, and with the ptarmigan slung over their gun barrels, the men trudged home through the arctic night.

Suddenly the scientists realized they were being followed—the pups' mother was tracking them. Wolves are normally fearful of man, but the female overcame her natural inclination to flee. Closer and closer she came until her nose nearly touched the ptarmigan that were dangling from the men's shoulders.

Unwilling to lose the precious young wolves they had worked so hard to collect for their studies, and not wishing to harm the mother, the men drove her off with snowballs.

When they finally reached camp, with pups, ptarmigan, and no harm done, they could see the female outside the circle of the camp, restlessly pacing. That night she kept vigil outside their tent. Not till morning did the female leave the dangerous precincts of man.

No Trespassing!

*Animals expend great energy keeping others out of the places they claim
for themselves. The competition for space reaches fever pitch
in the breeding season, when animals strive for enough room to rear a family*

"Free as a bird" is one of the least accurate interpretations that has ever been applied to animal behavior. Though the flight of a bird across the open skies suggests freedom of movement in both time and space, a bird, in common with most other animals on earth, lives according to the timetable peculiar to its species, and is as limited in where it may go as any plodding commuter.

Animals are generally tied to a particular habitat by food requirements. Ospreys, which feed mainly on fish, are seldom found far from seashores, lakes, or rivers. Bighorn sheep that graze on open, grassy slopes rarely stray into adjacent forests. The koala of Australia is found only where certain eucalyptus trees grow, for it depends entirely on their leaves for food.

Animals are restricted, too, by their ability to withstand heat or cold and their need for moisture: a tropical animal would die in the Arctic, and the river-dwelling hippopotamus would become dehydrated if stranded too long on dry land. Even altitude may have an influence. The vicuña, a dainty, agile animal resembling a small llama,

A young impala ram beats a hasty retreat before the charge of an outraged older male, owner of a harem. Possession of ewes is a full-time job for a male, for he must not only drive off poachers but must keep the females rounded up. Males without harems form bachelor herds.

is found only at elevations of 12,000 to 15,000 feet in the grasslands of the South American Andes.

But physical conditions do not tell the whole story. There are social factors that determine where animals live. The Laysan albatross and black-footed albatross have the flying power to cross any ocean, and could catch food in any sea. One of their traditional breeding sites is Midway Island in the Pacific Ocean.

Ever since Midway became a U.S. military airstrip, the albatrosses have frequently tangled with aircraft in their takeoffs and landings. Massive human efforts to discourage these birds from nesting on the island have been unsuccessful. They return every year in the face of smoke barrages and other harassments.

The albatrosses have no choice; they are responding to an ancestral urge. Individuals of every species must meet others of their kind if they are to breed. Some animals associate in permanent groups, others return periodically to traditional breeding grounds. For these populations of Laysan and black-footed albatrosses, one place of assembly is Midway Island, and it is unlikely to change. If the birds are finally ousted, they will be lost as a part of the breeding population. An individual albatross landing elsewhere in the breeding season would have little chance of finding a mate. The bird itself might survive, but it would not leave offspring. Whatever the risks to the individual, survival of the species has priority.

Spaced out with parade-ground precision, *gannet pairs nest on individual territories about two and a half feet apart. Once this rocky "aircraft carrier" off the coast of New Zealand is filled up, would-be nesters are driven off.*

Competition for Space

How animals lay claim to space is a key to many social systems in the animal kingdom. The numbers of animals generally increase to fill the available habitat, and every year more young are produced than can possibly find suitable living conditions. There is never enough space for all, thus animals must compete for a place in the sun.

It is apparent that animals need space to feed, sleep, mate, and rear their young free of intrusion. Less obvious is the almost universal need for "personal space." This sphere of control is a sort of "force field," which may completely surround the animal or may merely extend a short distance in front of its face.

Every relationship—between members of the same or opposite sex, and between parents and offspring—is expressed in how close one animal may come to another. Every encounter between individuals is marked by observance and adjustment of their spacing—or a dispute over it.

An animal's need for personal space remains fairly constant throughout the year. Even a bird in a flock appears to have a small personal space around it. Disputes arise only when neighbors approach too closely. Personal spacing can be seen among starlings and swallows perching on telephone wires; they distribute themselves at roughly even intervals.

In the breeding season, space requirements increase beyond the need for personal space; animals must have enough room to provide for their young. The hormones that bring birds into breeding conditions also affect their behavior. The first

An array of pigeons settles itself on winter-bare branches, catching the late afternoon sun. The regularity of spacing is remarkable and not accidental. If one pigeon gets too close to another, it is encouraged to move by sharp pecks.

expression of the need for space is that males become intolerant of one another. Many species of birds fly to traditional breeding grounds, where they vigorously compete for space.

Competition is often highly ritualized in both birds and mammals. In essence, one animal excludes others of its species from the space it claims for itself. Aggression is the means by which one animal forces another to back off and thereby acknowledge the claim.

Among the many species of animals, none has exactly the same pattern of spacing. Nevertheless, there are two broad categories: territories and home ranges. Most birds and many small mammals claim and defend a territory—it might be part of a marsh or field, the tops of several adjacent trees, a rock ledge, or the limb of a bush.

Territorial birds usually stake their claims only in the breeding season. Small mammals, on the other hand, often defend territories the year round, increasing their vigilance when they rear young. An African elephant shrew female excludes other elephant shrews from her burrow at all times, but when young are present, she becomes highly aggressive.

In territorial species, the competition results in two classes of animals, the "haves" and "have-nots." With the passage of time, established territories are accepted by all, the neighbors and the have-nots. Peace comes with acceptance—broken only by occasional disputes. If the fighting did not diminish, the value of the territories would be lost, for the animals would not have the freedom from interference that is essential for breeding.

The Home Range

The second major category of spacing is the home range. Home-ranging animals are familiar with, and move over, a large tract of land, defending a sphere around them wherever they are. In this way, many individuals of the same species may live in the same area, each using the trails and favored spots on its own timetable. The home-ranging pattern is most common among the mammals, though families of geese, ducks, or prairie chickens also use it. Home ranges are characteristic of solitary animals such as tigers, and of group-living species such as mountain goats and baboons.

The tiger roams over a large area of land on a fairly regular routine, visiting its water holes, favorite sunning rocks, or clearings where herds of deer feed. If prey animals are scarce, the home range of a male tiger may cover 600 square miles.

Female tigers have smaller home ranges, and several may live within the range of a male. When she has cubs, the tigress defends the area around the den in a territorial manner, but only until the young begin to accompany her on the hunt.

Because its home range is so large, the tiger could not possibly prevent other tigers from entering, and it doesn't try to do so. Thus the home ranges of the males may overlap without conflict,

and within those ranges, a female's range may overlap with those of other females, provided individuals remain on their established timetables.

The regularity of an animal's rounds, and its communication systems—calls, marks, and scents —help to ensure that it does not collide with others of its kind. The tiger's personal space is a sort of "portable territory," in that it excludes other tigers, or perhaps only others of the same sex, from the place where it is at any given time.

The lemurs of Madagascar live together in groups and move in regular patterns over their home ranges. Each troop leaves its nocturnal resting place at dawn and returns at nightfall. The troops seldom run afoul of one another because of the punctuality of their rounds.

Such a group of animals stays together because the individual animals never move more than a certain "social distance" from their fellows. In large migratory or winter flocks of birds, the tendency to maintain this social distance seems to be the only force that binds the individuals of a species together.

But in smaller groups of gregarious animals, individuals recognize one another and are bound together, not only by the maintenance of social distance, but by a strong social structure. Rather than the haves and have-nots of the territorial

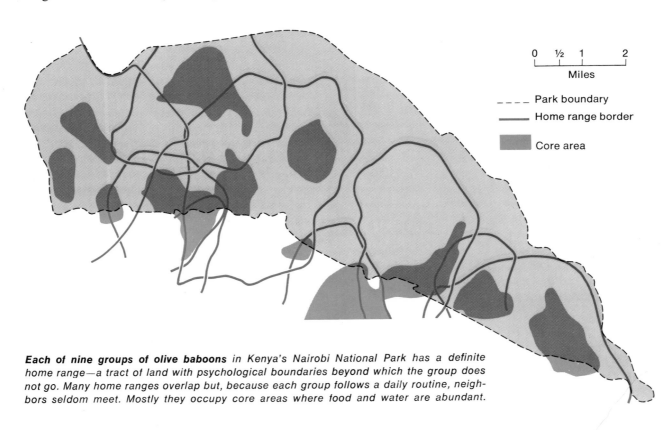

0 ½ 1 2
Miles

_ _ _ _ Park boundary

——— Home range border

▓ Core area

Each of nine groups of olive baboons in Kenya's Nairobi National Park has a definite home range—a tract of land with psychological boundaries beyond which the group does not go. Many home ranges overlap but, because each group follows a daily routine, neighbors seldom meet. Mostly they occupy core areas where food and water are abundant.

system, each animal may have a particular rank. In these hierarchies—called peck orders or dominance systems—an individual gains highest rank by fighting for it. When the animal has won, it has precedence in all the activities of the group.

Below the dominant individuals are subordinates, which in turn are dominant over others, all the way down to the lowest-ranking individual, which must give way in any encounter. The highest-ranking animal is called the "alpha," the lowest, the "omega," after the first and last letters of the Greek alphabet.

The highest-ranking monkey, the alpha male, has freedom to move at will through the troop; all others give him room. The lowest-ranking individual, the omega, has the least freedom. It must acknowledge and avoid the personal space of all others. It often finds the least opposition from troop members when it remains at the edge of the group—where there is also the greatest danger from predators.

Some species exhibit a combination of territorial and home-ranging behavior. The brush-tailed opossum of Australia is a solitary mammal that defends its small nesting site as a territory year round. By day it sleeps in its nest, and at night it moves unchallenged through an intricate world of pathways, trees, and branches. The trail it follows is a kind of linear home range that others are free to travel, as long as each observes its own schedule.

And there are other, informal "arrangements" that occur when territorial or home-ranging animals of the same species meet beyond their own realms. The Steller's jay of California moves over a large area to feed. The farther it flies from its nest, the less it is inclined to attack other jays. When it approaches the nest of another jay, it becomes increasingly timid. In a sense, a boundary does exist about equidistant between the nests of neighbors, but it does not restrict the movements of the birds. Their ranges are much larger than the territories they defend.

If a feeding station is placed in the forest in the vicinity of the nests of several Steller's jays, the bird with the nearest nest has priority over all other birds at the feeding station. The jay with the next-nearest nest has second rank, and can chase away others when the first bird is absent. The system of dominance is like the peck order of chickens, except that while the ranks of jays change when the location of the feeding station is changed, the ranks in a flock of chickens remain the same wherever the flock may be.

Enough Room to Hunt

A stoat is about twice as large as a weasel, but its home range is eight times larger than that of the weasel. The stoat needs more room because it hunts above ground, while the weasel is able to pursue the same prey into underground burrows.

The five-pound pine marten specializes in hunting red squirrels and snowshoe hares, and needs about seven square miles to support itself. But a ten-pound fox, which feeds on more kinds of animals, can find enough to eat in one square mile.

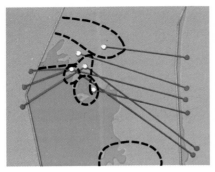

For mating and nesting. *Canada geese establish well-defined territories for mating and nesting. With loud hisses and aggressive postures, they warn neighbors that trespassing will not be tolerated. Yet, even in the breeding season, they mingle with flockmates at feeding sites outside territorial boundaries.*

Different Territories for Different Life Styles

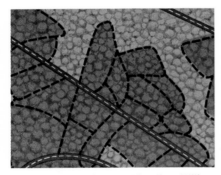

For mating, nesting, and feeding. *Willow warblers, like most songbirds, mate, nest, and feed in territories from which other members of the species are excluded—till the breeding season ends.*

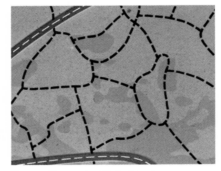

For mating only. *Male black grouse establish mating territories, called leks, in the breeding season. Females briefly enter, mate, then depart to lay their eggs and raise their young elsewhere.*

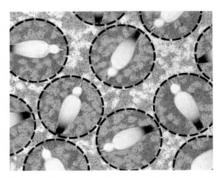

For nesting only. *Many seabirds, such as gulls, terns, and cormorants, hold only tiny nesting territories. Boundaries are commonly determined by how far sitting birds can reach out to peck neighbors.*

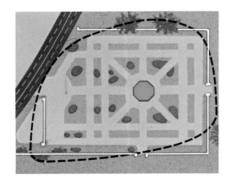

For feeding only. *Male ruby-throated hummingbirds often stake out feeding territories—here, a quarter-acre flower garden. An "owner" chases out not only hummingbirds but moths and bees too!*

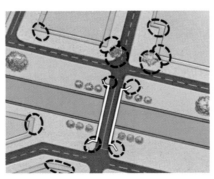

For roosting only. *By day starlings congregate in vast flocks, but at nightfall each bird returns to its own roosting territory—a specific spot on a tree limb or the ledge of a building or bridge.*

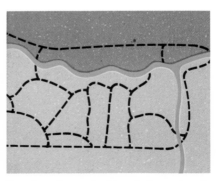

For the winter. *Red-headed woodpeckers do not migrate. Each bird sets up a winter territory with a roost hole and several caches of acorns, which it defends against jays and other poachers.*

Depending on species, a bird's territory may be large, small, or portable, but in each case it is hotly defended

For most songbirds, the territory serves the entire breeding cycle—the claiming of a mate, building of a nest, and rearing of young. Its benefit is primarily in guaranteeing seclusion for the offspring and a readily accessible food supply. A territorial male and his mate do not have to forage into unknown areas. As the nestlings hatch, the importance of this food preserve increases, especially among species that feed their young at frequent intervals; little time is wasted searching for food, and there is a minimum of competition for the supply.

A typical songbird territory is that held by the European robin. The male puffs out his red breast and sings from a song post, usually where a hedge or trees at the edge of a clearing provide perches. Ownership of a territory makes the male eligible to the female, who arrives after the males have set up territories. Courtship takes place within its precincts.

The male's territorial song notifies other male robins of his claim, and they respond from their territories with songs and postures. At first, there are incessant boundary disputes between neighbors. Each male patrols the borders of his acre and a half, which is an average-size territory for a European robin.

Territorial defense is usually confined to loud singing and chasing, but if an invader is particularly persistent, the combatants may come to blows, clawing and pecking furiously.

Probably the owner of the territory will win the fight, but if he doesn't, the female robin will stay in the territory and mate with the interloper. The attraction of a male robin for a female seems to depend entirely on his ability to hold a territory.

The bishop bird, an African weaver finch whose territory also serves the full breeding cycle, builds several nests, to each of which he attracts a female. As one female is mated and settled on her eggs, he courts another. The pressures on his landholding are great because of the large numbers of offspring that must be fed.

The territories of colonial-nesting seabirds are commonly small, and serve only for courtship and nesting, not as food preserves. Gannets, puffins, and gulls feed in the sea, an area impossible to claim and defend in a territorial manner—the turbulent waves offer no landmarks or points from which a bird could "take a stand." The elegant tern, which nests along the coastal dunes on islands off Baja California, holds a tiny territory, just a nest with hardly enough room around it for the bird to jab its beak. Courtship takes place there, and later, rearing of the offspring.

Male birds of paradise and bowerbirds claim territories that are used only for courtship and mating. Birds of paradise aggregate in trees, each holding a single branch, where they posture and call to attract females. The bowers, arenas, and maypoles of bowerbirds are widely spaced out; these elaborate structures serve to attract females to mate, and are never used as nests. After mating, the females of these species go off into the surrounding forest to build a nest, lay eggs, and rear the offspring unaided.

Following the Food Supply

The cattle egret, so named because the bird feeds by walking beside grazing animals, holds a "portable" feeding territory. It snaps up the insects that are disturbed by the movement of the cattle. Each bird defends its position to the right or left side of a particular cow or bull as the animal grazes. This mobile "territory" is established on a day-to-day basis. Similarly, the bicolored antbirds of the South American rain forests take up territories each day around the moving front of a horde of army ants. The birds feed on the swarms of insects stirred up by the march.

Birds of prey, which feed on other birds, fish, and small mammals, have nesting territories, but they feed over a huge area in much the same way as seabirds feed at sea. A small defendable area would not contain enough prey animals to satisfy the appetites of the osprey or hawk and its young, so their system amounts to a home range with defense confined to the area around the nest.

Birds that lead their young away from the nest in search of food usually forsake all territorial behavior as soon as the young hatch. The availability of food in an area is generally the main limitation of their movement. Families of geese adopt the home-range way of life, swimming together in lake or stream, and feeding in the lush grasses lining the banks of lakes and streams or grazing in meadows nearby. Families are spaced out, but if they should come too close to one another, both sets of parents rush forth to "shout threats" until spacing has been restored.

A young male vervet backs away from a dominant female as fast as he can go. Having approached too closely, he is driven off with threats—including the aggressive vervet stare. The brow is raised, revealing the white eye-rings.

Retreat is difficult, for if an animal turns its back, it may be nipped. A second female assists the first in the attack, as a dominant male stands and watches. One scared infant cowers while another scoots away from the ruckus.

The Paradox of Aggression

The word "aggression"—meaning the attack of one individual on another—has strong human overtones that are not applicable to animals. Though aggression is deplorable among people and nations, among animals it is usually strictly utilitarian. They could not exist without aggressive behavior.

Most of the fighting in the world occurs between two animals of the same species. Its objective, more often than not, is a contest for control of the space around whatever the animals need—nest sites, food, and mates. Fighting normally results in the loser taking flight.

Hunting animals are often called aggressive because they use their powerful teeth or claws to attack their prey. But hunting should not be equated with aggression between individuals of the same species, for the outcome is different.

Natural selection has built into the behavior of most species a strong inhibition against killing their own kind. There is a wide range of rituals that regulate aggression between individuals of the same species. All-out fights take enormous energy, which is better used in other activities. The survival of a species is served as much by the fact that an individual can lose without being killed as it is by the ability of some to win. If a vanquished individual lives to fight another day, it may win the next round. In every species there are "rules" of fighting that are seldom violated.

Obviously there are not—and cannot be—any such rules when a pack of Cape hunting dogs attack a gazelle; the dogs are intent on killing for food. Nor are there any built-in inhibitions governing the way a prey animal fights off a predator. It is a "no-holds-barred" situation in which the attacker is driven off by whatever means the victim is able to muster.

When two animals of the same species fight, one gains the prize—whether space or mates—and the defeated animal either flees or acknowledges defeat. In any case, the fight is over for a time, and the winner is able to enjoy the fruits of its victory. Thus the paradox of aggression is that it is a peace-keeping force.

No animal simply attacks at the sight of a rival. When the intruder comes too close, a formal ritual may begin, with the advance met by a mild threat. If the challenger crosses the territorial boundary or enters the personal space of the resident, the threat becomes more pronounced. A continued advance finally provokes retaliation, and the animals square off for a fight.

Whether the sequence from threat to assault is sudden or slow, the pattern is consistent in each species in a given situation. Some animals attack so swiftly that there seems hardly any threat to warn the intruder. On the other hand, the overture to a fight between two Grant's gazelles is a stately parade.

The two male gazelles eye one another from a distance, each assuming a stiff-legged stance that displays its size and horns and allows an assessment of strength. If neither animal withdraws, they approach with their heads turned to the side, giving the opponent a full view of the horns. They come alongside, nodding horns, then hold up their heads and display their white throats. Now that each has sized up the potential prowess of his opponent, a gazelle that does not want to fight may simply keep going.

If neither gazelle leaves, they raise and lower their heads repeatedly in the throat display. If this fails to settle the issue, a nose-on examination may convince one that the other is too strong to fight. If not, they lock horns and a pushing contest begins, ending when the weaker of the two leaps back, disengaging his horns. Two evenly matched gazelles may wear themselves out as they struggle across the dusty plains.

Injury is rare, though fighting always involves risk. The advantage of preliminary threats is that they avert a great deal of fighting, because the dominance of one animal is acknowledged at an early stage. Often the animal's fur stands up, which makes it look larger than it really is. A threatening domestic cat erects its fur from head to tail, and often turns sideways, which shows its bulk. The wolf also seems to swell in size, head and ears up, great neck ruff erect, fangs bared, and shoulder hair bristling. Many birds, like the fighting cock, erect the feathers on their necks.

It is easy to recognize the threat in the snarls and crouching of two leopards. When a male caribou lays back his ears, curls his nose, and lowers his head, his intention is unmistakably hostile. But it took scientists a long while to realize that many of the subtle gestures of animals are threatening. A vervet monkey has a dark face and light eyelids, and threatens by raising its brow and staring so that the eyelids are displayed. The direct stare of an adult baboon is a strong reprimand to an unruly juvenile.

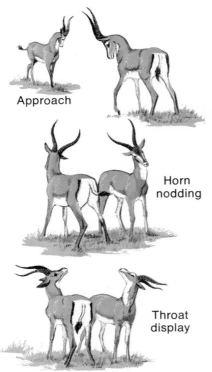

Approach

Horn nodding

Throat display

A Grant's gazelle gives its opponent every opportunity to withdraw before the going gets rough. Slowly, ceremoniously, two males approach, nod heads, and display their throats in ritual threat. If this fails, they lock horns in combat (right).

Though hostile gestures are common, blood-letting is rare. Many animals give up before the fight starts

The remarkable thing about animal aggression is not how much damage animals inflict on one another, but how little. The African cane rat, which has deadly, razor-sharp teeth, seldom uses them in a direct confrontation with another cane rat. Head to head, the two animals shove in what looks like a full-body Indian wrestling match. Back and forth they go, pushing vigorously.

Domestic cats do most of their fighting with their paws. Their claws are formidable weapons, but not so lethal as their canine teeth. Cats seem to exercise considerable restraint in biting around the opponent's face—perhaps because each animal must protect its own eyes. Damage to the fighters tends to be concentrated on the shoulders, where heavy muscles protect vital parts.

This is not to say that animals never fight to the death. A lion intruding on the territory of a pride may be killed in a swift, merciless battle. More commonly, death is accidental. In a fight between two impalas or two American bison, the jab of a horn may pierce an opponent in a vital spot. The loser, or even the winner, may die from the wounds later, or be so weakened that it becomes an easy target for a predator.

At any point in the rising tempo of hostility, one animal may break away and flee. Behavior that halts a fight is called submission. Flight, a universal form of submission, removes an animal from the territory or personal space of the victor.

On the African plains, a hartebeest lives with a group of females during the breeding season. A second buck without a harem may intrude; if he is detected, a wild chase ensues. The pursuer halts at his own territorial border. The chase is over, for the vanishing escapee is no threat once he is past the boundary.

An elephant, on the other hand, does not hold a territory. When males fight, the lumbering loser can seldom escape quickly enough from the per-

Scuffing the earth and shrieking with rage, two black rhinos confront one another. Most rhino aggression is all show, but these males were actually fighting. When one turned away, defeated, the winner could have gored him but did not do so.

sonal space of his pursuer to avoid thumps on his sides and hindquarters. The pursuer belabors his victory with trunk and tusks until the loser succeeds in putting a considerable distance between them.

Continual chases are not practical among group-living animals. They would take both antagonists outside the safety limits of the group. Nor can there be constant fighting. The settling of differences takes other, more subtle, forms.

A subordinate male bison or yak can pass or cross in front of a dominant male without being attacked. The subordinate uses a signal hardly detectable to a human observer—lowered eyelashes—whenever entering the personal space of the dominant individual. This is appeasement behavior, which inhibits threats.

Young Barbary ape males have a delightful appeasing procedure. One puts an infant on his back, then approaches an old patriarch. The infant is a passport of sorts, for the dominant animal will groom it, and not threaten or attack its carrier.

A wolf may approach the pack leader appeasingly, head and ears down, eyes averted, tail between its legs. Looking small and behaving inoffensively, the subordinate cancels any affront in his approach.

If an individual fails to behave appeasingly and is attacked, it can call off the fight by signaling defeat—that is, taking a submissive posture. Even in midfight, a wolf can inhibit the attack of another by freezing. It stands motionless, its neck inches from the victor's jaws. A bite on the neck could kill the animal, and yet the winner never bites. A motionless stance, it seems, removes the stimulus for attack.

Another submissive gesture is for a wolf to lie on its back, exposing its abdomen to be licked. This is juvenile behavior used in an adult situation—a fight. The submitting wolf benefits from the fact that adults do not attack juveniles.

Males rarely attack females, either. In some species, a distinctively female posture sometimes serves as submissive behavior, allowing the loser to remain beside the victor without further attack. Most of the Old World monkeys and apes use a female posture of sexual presentation to express submission.

Prancing on a mountaintop in Italy, ibex rams pull in their chins and show off their impressive horns. If neither ram backs down, they butt heads. Like many other goats, ibex fight enthusiastically year round, with no apparent damage.

The Efficient Sign Languages of Animals

Human beings will probably never "talk to the animals," but it is possible to "read" them. Most animals use postures that communicate their feelings with perfect accuracy. They are even able to express doubt. Members of the same species un-derstand what the flip of a feather or the raising of fur means, and often "reply" with a change of stance. Expressions may be extreme or mild, showing aggression or fear, and sometimes an animal simply broadcasts its presence to others of its kind.

The Angle of Attack

The crest of a Steller's jay expresses how the bird feels. When its feathers stand straight up, the bird is furious. When the crest is flat, the jay is at peace with the world. Intermediate positions give fine shading to the bird's signals.

Cause for Alarm

A male zebra finch expresses readiness to attack by taking a torpedo-like, horizontal posture. A bolt-upright stance also shows hostility, but with an element of fear; he may flee rather than fight. A submissive female fluffs up her feathers and crouches like a helpless, rather frumpy infant.

A Complex Signaling System

The "at ease" posture of a wolf is tail hanging, ears forward, and brow unfurrowed. When a wolf threatens, its tail and ears go up. Growling and snarling, it exhibits its teeth. The way another wolf forestalls attack is by behaving submissively; it turns back its ears and tucks its tail between its legs.

Normal   Threat   Submission

Decisions! Decisions!

In a tense situation, an animal may have an impulse to attack, and at the same time, a wish to flee. While it sizes up the sit-uation, the animal may engage in some seemingly inappropri-ate activity, which is called displacement behavior. A chick-en may feed, a monkey yawn, or a rat scratch itself.

A gull that finds itself in a perplexing situation may turn aside and pull grass, behavior borrowed from nest-building.

An uncertain oystercatcher may express its confusion by swiv-eling its head around and assuming the posture of sleep.

The Highly Communicative Conduct of a Cat

INCREASING AGGRESSION →

↓ INCREASING FEAR

A confident cat (upper left), feeling neither hostile nor fearful, generally walks with its tail down and its ears erect. At the sight of another cat in the distance, its hindquarters may rise and its tail begin to arch. If a cat is frightened and does not want to fight, it crouches (lower left). But if the animal feels endangered, it fights in full battle array—tail up, ears down, fur standing, claws at the ready (lower right). A fearful, hostile cat also has impressive vocal weaponry. Its yowls and hisses are an important part of its defense. The transition from one mood to another may take place in seconds, or the cat may pause a moment, undecided, with fear and hostility in a rough balance (center).

The Versatile Trunk of the Elephant

INCREASING AGGRESSION

An elephant swings its trunk in a manner that seems quite casual, snuffing here and there, exploring the ground and picking up food. But the trunk has other uses. Irritated by the behavior of a subordinate, a dominant elephant issues a mild warning by lifting its head. A straight, level trunk is a serious threat. But when it is pointed in the air, it's an announcement of mayhem. A frightened elephant curls the tip of the trunk. Gradually, as its fear increases, the curling becomes more pronounced. Finally, the terrified animal almost ties its trunk in a knot.

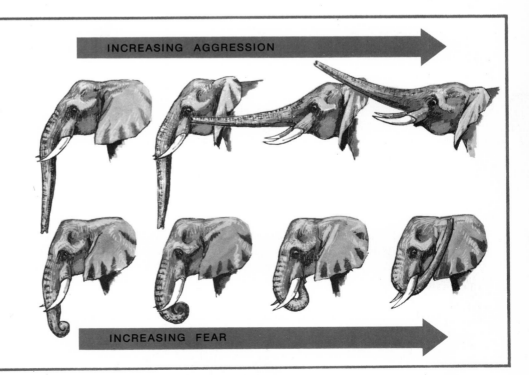

INCREASING FEAR

A black oystercatcher asserts its territorial rights with a shrill piping cry. The cry is taken up by others—opponents and bystanders—each threatening with downward-pointing bill and a rapid up-and-down pumping of its body.

Sounding a Warning

Animals have many ways of announcing their presence to others of their species. Birds do so by calls or songs, and by postures or movements. A house sparrow attracts attention with a chirp and a flip of the tail when it lands. The observer may be a mate, a young have-not, or a territorial neighbor. To each, the same message has a different meaning. The mate is reassured and is able to keep close. A young trespasser becomes instantly still and alert, ready to flee. A neighboring bird that hears the territorial proclamation (sounds never made by a trespasser) will probably answer with a burst of song.

The vocal and visual signals of birds are seldom used independently. The European skylark delivers songs of surpassing beauty as it spirals into the air. Its outpouring contrasts strongly with the drab appearance of the bird itself. Conversely, birds with especially showy plumage seldom have elaborate songs. A bird of paradise, which has a highly developed display, has only a small repertoire of loud, ringing calls. Between these extremes, the majority of birds have a less spectacular blend of vocal and display behavior.

When a cock crows, it always adopts a crowing posture, head and tail erect, and wings stretched downward in a smooth, well-integrated combination of signals. The cardinal male, which requires an exposed dead branch as a fixed commanding perch, uses it as an essential part of his territory for the delivery of his song.

There is a daily rhythm to song; it is usually most pronounced at dawn and dusk. The birds with territories devote a set period of time to proclaiming their ownership and, at the same time, receiving the messages of their neighbors. This frees them for other activities during the remainder of the day, though naturally they will resist an intruder at any time.

The intensity of bird song varies throughout the year; it is usually strongest in spring when the need for a territory is greatest. The bird's song is important in establishing a territory and attracting a mate. Singing continues into summer when the territory is held for rearing the young, but birds do not sing while on the nest. The sound might attract an enemy. Singing usually diminishes when birds give up their individual territories after the breeding season, especially in the temperate climes.

In a dense woodland, the song of a male wren rings out with great vigor. Though it occupies a territory of only two or three acres, the tiny, inconspicuous bird fills the woodland with his song of ownership. Usually, an intruder entering

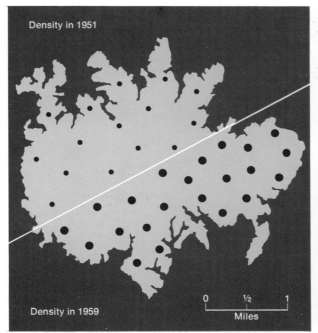

Density in 1951

Density in 1959

0   ½   1
Miles

Following an epidemic, the howler monkey population of Barro Colorado Island in Panama went from a low of 237 in 1951 to 814 in 1959. The map indicates how the populations were spaced. A male shows the jaw structure that produces the din.

his territory is silent and furtive. If it is noticed, the wren increases his vocal efforts, and the trespasser usually responds to the heightened threat by fleeing. Only after the vocal assault fails will the wren attack the intruder.

At any point in the hostilities, the intruder may give up. Actual beak-to-beak combat is rare. Like the caterwauling of tomcats on the back fence, the noisy threats of birds are mostly bluff.

The intensity of territorial defense is not uniform over the whole area. Generally, the closer a trespasser comes to the nest or other favorite place, the more aggressive is the landholder and the more violently will trespassers be punished.

In the heat of combat, when a territory holder pursues the enemy beyond his own boundaries, the situation suddenly changes. The defender becomes less confident, and if the chase brings the two birds onto the territory of the original intruder, their roles are reversed. The intruder becomes an indignant property owner, and the owner of the first territory a harried fugitive.

Many mammals, like birds, are highly vocal in their territorial behavior. They yowl, screech, growl, hiss, spit, and whine. Howler monkeys of the South American rain forests are among the noisiest mammals of all. With large, bony resonating chambers under their jaws, the males

make loud, deep howls, and the females give sharp barks like terriers.

At daybreak, the whole troop howls. At the first howl, all the members join in. Neighboring troops immediately take up the cry, and the forest rings with their calls. The ranges of howlers overlap; only the core area, containing favored sleeping trees, is used exclusively by one troop. At the edge of their range, howlers seem defensive.

Howlers continually travel over their ranges, feeding on leaves, buds, and fruit. They are intolerant of other troops of howlers, and will howl lustily at their approach. Direct encounters are rare; if their paths cross, usually one group has the right of way.

One day during a storm, three separate troops of howlers were observed converging on a ravine. The sounds of their approach were apparently masked by the driving rain. Suddenly finding themselves mixed in with members of other troops, the startled animals ran in all directions. A cacophony of howling, barking, and whining rose above the sound of the rain, as excited males, juveniles, and females clutching their infants raced to and fro in confusion. The troops separated without fighting. For howlers, sound is an effective—and definitely preferred—means of claiming space.

Scent Signals

It may offend the fastidiousness of human beings to see the frank interest animals take in their own waste products. But it is not lack of "cleanliness" that prompts a dog to sniff its own feces or the urine of other dogs left at the curb.

Dogs, like most other mammals, have a far keener sense of smell than human beings. The depositing of urine and feces serves the animal as a highly efficient means of communication, for the scents are all individual. A dog's scent on a tree or hydrant signals its presence in the area, and the scents of other dogs at the same sites identify all the animals in the neighborhood to each other.

In the wild the scents of mammals serve a function similar to the calls and songs of birds, except that a scent mark lasts longer. Scents are used by both territorial and home-ranging animals. The other residents of the area are aware of who passed by, and probably how long ago.

There is a remarkable assemblage of hippopotamuses in the Congo's Rwindi-Rutshuru National Park. The hippopotamuses may be found in the Rutshuru River, grouped into large tribes, each headed by a dominant male. In a stretch of thirty miles, there are approximately 3000 of these huge animals, all in their own places.

Except in the mating season, hippo males occupy exclusive territories on the banks of the river; females collect to feed on larger territories with their offspring, including juvenile males that have not yet claimed an area. The territories are pear-shaped, with a narrow section toward the river that serves as a ramp.

At nightfall, usually at the same time each evening, a hippo trudges up his ramp toward the pasture that is his feeding territory. At various places along the way, and particularly along trails, the male marks shrubs with his individual signature. He pauses, raises his tail, and noisily shoots a stream of excreta mixed with urine toward the bushes. The foul-smelling stuff is scattered widely by the propeller-like movements of the tail. The identity of the owner of this particular plot of ground can be recognized by all visiting hippos.

Such practices are common among mammals, more so among males than females, and marking is more pronounced in the breeding season than at other times of the year. In most cases, the resident has the right to mark; the interloper does not. Though the owner may be absent, its scent remains as a long-term reminder to others that trespassers will be prosecuted.

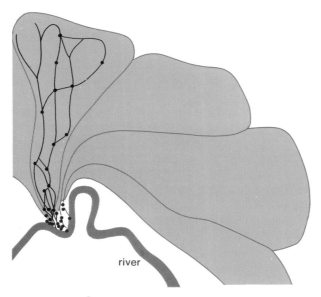

Female hippos and their young march up a common ramp from an African river to broad feeding areas on the banks. The hippos' territories, which fan out from the ramp, are pear-shaped, with females collecting on the larger ones and individual males occupying slightly smaller holdings. The lines on the territory at left show the trails followed by one male in his evening rounds; the circles show where he deposits his scent, warning others to keep out.

A brown lemur makes his way through the trees, marking frequently as he goes. Lemurs, residents of Madagascar, have scent glands on wrists and shoulders. Some species wipe scent on their tails and brandish them to threaten others.

Many mammals have scent glands that are also used for marking. They are usually located on those parts of the body that come into contact with the animal's world. Lemurs mark with wrists and paws as they climb through the branches where they live. One species, the ring-tailed lemur, has scent glands on its forearms and shoulders. When it is aggressive, it wipes its forearms across the shoulders, then repeatedly rubs its long tail between its forearms, so that the scents of both glands are on the tail.

Many burrowing animals drag their hindquarters on the ground, scenting their territories with glands located in the anal region. Several species of deer have scent glands under their eyes which they use to rub their scent on trees or brush. The American white-tailed deer marks with glands on its hoofs or legs. Bears have scent glands on their necks; they also scratch the trunks of trees and chew the bark, thus leaving a visual signal and the scent of their saliva.

Some animals have several scent glands located on different parts of their bodies. The marmot, or woodchuck, marks with its anal glands, but it has other glands around its eyes and on its cheeks; their uses are not yet understood.

European rabbits have anal scent glands, but instead of dragging to mark the ground they secrete the scent on their feces. Fecal pellets are scented only when deposited in small dunghills along the rabbit's pathways, and not when dropped at random around the territory. The dunghills serve as territorial markers.

Rabbits also have a gland located under the chin that secretes a fluid with a distinctive odor. As it patrols the boundary of its colony, the rabbit constantly sniffs and leaves its scent, either by depositing pellets on dunghills or by "chinning" logs or patches of grass. Rabbits chin only in their own territories. The male is more active in chinning than the female; the underside of his chin is frequently matted with secretions.

Its own scent is undoubtedly reassuring to the mammal marking its territory or home range, as is song to a songbird. Even if the scent is stale, the animal recognizes it. When armadillos were first brought to zoos, a failure to understand their need to be surrounded by their own scents led to the death of several of the animals. The male armadillo marks extensively with its urine. With the best intentions in the world, the keepers would assiduously clean the armadillos' cages, obliterating or masking the scents, and the armadillos would set about at once to mark the enclosures again. These misguided efforts were finally brought to an end in more than one case when the poor animal died of dehydration.

It is only after an animal's warning system has failed—whether it be the song of a bird, the scent of a mammal, or the howls of a monkey troop— that animals resort to more active threats and perhaps to actual fighting.

A ritual of grunting and raking with front hoofs precedes the charge of bighorn rams. These 250-pounders

drop down as they lunge, building up to a speed equivalent to a car crashing into a stone wall at forty-five miles an hour. As the

Two zebra stallions fight for possession of a harem, biting at the neck and striking with their hoofs.

Fighting Is the Last Resort

When threats fail, animals attack one another in the manner characteristic of their species —biting, scratching, kicking, or pushing. Combat is seldom fatal, for individuals seem to know when to quit. Some fighting is perplexing: Male and female bighorn sheep spar constantly, but the "winner" doesn't seem to win anything.

Rearing back in the dust of an East African game reserve, two superb starlings scratch and peck over a scrap of food.

rams collide, the mountains echo with the rifle report of bone on bone. They stand stunned for a few seconds, then back off for another bash.

Roosters slash at one another with needle-sharp spurs—sometimes with lethal results.

Elephant bulls settle the question of dominance by a ponderous pushing contest. The only real danger comes when the weaker animal accepts defeat and breaks off the fight: In turning away to flee, he is exposed to the tusks of the winner.

Rushing to the defense of his harem, *a male elephant seal drives a poacher back. Combatants may be cut, but few are killed in such encounters. However, in his haste, the charging bull may leave a wake of crushed pups behind him.*

Dominance in a group is won by combat. And some animals settle who's who right down to the lowest individual

Among large mammals, particularly grazing species, competition during the breeding season may be to claim and defend a number of females. Since the animals feed over a large area, the males cannot restrict the females to one place. Some species such as the water buffalo follow a herd of females and keep them from becoming separated. Though the water buffalo bull or the impala buck does not defend a territory, woe betide any male that tries to approach his harem.

Wildebeest may actually migrate during the rutting season, and as the herd moves, the males maneuver females into groups that vary in size from a few animals to as many as 150. The females, regardless of the size of the harem, generally seem indifferent to the activities of the males. They mate willingly with the one claiming the harem, whether he is the male who formed it or a successful challenger.

At the beginning of the breeding season, the first southern elephant seals to leave the sea and haul themselves up on the shore are the oldest, strongest bulls. They are fourteen years old or more, about fourteen feet long, and have a fully developed proboscis—an elaborate nose with deep creases running crosswise. Next come the bachelors, the younger males that begin their initiation into adult society at about the age of six. They are smaller, with shallower creases on their snouts.

Older bulls that have had harems in previous seasons are called beachmasters. The groups of males—beachmasters and bachelors—lie basking in peaceful groups for several weeks, until the cow elephant seals arrive in groups of two to four, a few days before their pups are born.

The peaceful mood changes as the beachmasters and bachelors vie with one another to collect harems of cows. Fighting among males is a noisy, bloody business. The bulls begin combat with mighty bellowing through the proboscis. Propped upright on their flippers, two males come to within inches of one another, trumpeting with tremendous force. If neither retreats, the males slash at each other's throats with powerful teeth. Many scars decorate the necks of beachmasters. Young bachelors are easily put to rout, and they take refuge with a group of other unsuccessful males. A defeated bull in retreat is never pursued.

Only a dominant female rabbit may nest in the security of the colony's central warren. Lower-ranking females nest at the outskirts, exposed to greater danger. Rabbits warn off intruders by leaving scented pellets on paths around the colony.

An experienced beachmaster can round up many of the small groups of females with great efficiency. If the harem is small, it is exclusively held by one male; only he mates with the females. More often the harems are large, consisting of from 300 to 600 cows, and there are usually several such harems on any one beach.

When there are more than fifty cows in a harem, another male, or perhaps two or three, joins the beachmaster, so that a very large group of cows is attended by several bulls. Strictly speaking, these assemblies can no longer be called harems but, rather, polygamous mating groups.

The colony is a deafening collection of elephant seals in constant turmoil. Within the social structure, the females and young are free of interference by the many young males outside. When a cow wanders, the beachmaster or one of his assistants retrieves her, picking her up by the loose skin on the back and neck and slinging her back into the group.

Membership in the harem of a particular bull changes from year to year. The beachmaster must begin his work anew each breeding season, for the cows apparently do not recognize a particular male, or attempt to join any specific harem.

Though spectacular, this dominance system is essentially simple. The strongest bulls prevent the mating of younger or weaker bulls, thus ensuring that only the strong have offspring. At the same time, the young males are tolerated so long as they do not enter the harem area. The fighting of elephant seal males is seldom fatal.

Many mammals have a more highly structured dominance system than elephant seals. Among the wild rabbits of Europe, male and female hierarchies are established at the beginning of the breeding season. Males and females gain status through a series of fights. The highest-ranking doe, the alpha, has the privilege of nesting in the colony's central warren or burrow. This is her territory, within the territory of the male, and is the safest location for a nest. As a result, the alpha doe is generally the most successful breeder. She has more litters a year, perhaps four, and the survival rate of her offspring is higher than that of lower-ranking females.

The lowest-ranking female, the omega doe, is forced to nest on the outskirts of the colony in a shallow, scooped-out burrow. She has a lower breeding rate, and her offspring are more vulnerable to predators.

The dominant buck rabbit defends the territory within which his group lives. His dominance is expressed by chasing subordinates. There are generally fewer male rabbits than females in any colony, and the males have a greater tendency to enforce their status than females do. The rabbit "kittens" share the rank of their mother, and if the kittens of an omega doe enter the main burrow, they are attacked by the alpha doe.

The free-ranging primates are not restricted by attachment to burrows and pathways; the position of a monkey in its troop depends primarily on accumulated experience in social encounters with every troop member. Because they mature slowly, individuals progress through many social roles from newborn infant to aging adult.

Like the European rabbit, olive baboons have two separate hierarchies, one male, one female. But dominant males have the greater authority. They exert their dominance more by threat and chasing than by actual physical attack.

Dominant baboons have priority in mating, particularly when the females are fully into estrus —the period during which females can conceive. The females, too, have a ranking system; some hold high rank at all times. But during estrus, even a low-ranking female gains status by associating with the dominant males. When she gives birth, and while her offspring is young, she is again accorded high status because the high-ranking animals are solicitous toward her infant.

The dominant male baboon is the universal protector of the weak; he will intervene on behalf of youngsters if they are threatened by adults, and he holds in check the tyranny of a dominant female who is making life miserable for a subordinate female. His presence inhibits any aggressive behavior that might disrupt the group.

In all primate groups, the dominance system is strongly influenced by the individual "personalities" of the animals. Some dominant males are despotic, while others may be almost benign. In some groups, the cooperation between two dominant males is so amiable that it is impossible to be certain which, if either, is subordinate. By such cooperation, both animals acquire higher status than either could alone. Such personal relationships, or "alliances," have been observed in other species as well, particularly among jackdaws, a European relative of the crow.

An impala male does not defend a particular territory; the herd roams over a wide area of African savanna. The male's defense is of his harem—commonly fifteen to twenty ewes with their young, but sometimes as many as 100.

Peck Orders in Chickens

When adult chickens are put together in a flock, they invariably form a hierarchy, or peck order. So automatic is this behavior among fowl that when they are reared together in a brooder, a peck order starts to develop among the chicks in the second week, and is well established by the time they are eight weeks old.

The rank of each individual chicken is determined by a series of contests, one at a time, between each male and all other males, and each female and all other females. Once the flock has established its male and female hierarchies, the conflict subsides. Hierarchies, like territories, bring an end to fighting. Birds of high rank have precedence at feeding and watering troughs, at nests and roosts, and can move about with considerable freedom. The more dominant roosters sire most of the chicks.

There is a clear correlation between the stability of the peck order in the flock and the productivity of the birds. When fighting is prevalent, males are less active sexually, and egg production drops, for many of the hens low in rank cease to lay altogether. When a stranger—either rooster or hen—is introduced into an established flock, the newcomer is vigorously attacked, and usually defeated. It is often prevented from approaching the food and watering troughs, and chased continuously.

Chickens recognize one another by their heads—the shapes of their combs and color of their feathers. When the heads of dominant chickens were disguised in an experiment, they lost their high status at once, and were attacked as though they were strangers. But when the disguises were removed, all regained their former status.

In the wild, a jungle rooster crows to proclaim his territory during the breeding season. Soon a neighboring rooster arrives at their common boundary and together the two parade in parallel formation about seventy feet apart, crowing loudly. Should the dominant rooster die, another rooster immediately takes over the flock. Usually, the rooster is replaced from within his own flock; the next male in the peck order takes control.

The Despotic Rule of a Rooster

In a study of feral chickens (birds that were once domesticated but now live in the wild) it was found that chickens live by rules as intricate as those governing the court of Louis XIV. The dominant rooster prevents fighting among subordinates in his vicinity. To have a fight, females must move ten feet away, males sixty. A subordinate male is not allowed to mate with a hen unless he finds her at a distance of fifty or sixty feet from the reigning male of the flock.

Subordinate males fight far away from the dominant rooster.

A departing subordinate male straightens up, flaps his wings, and crows.

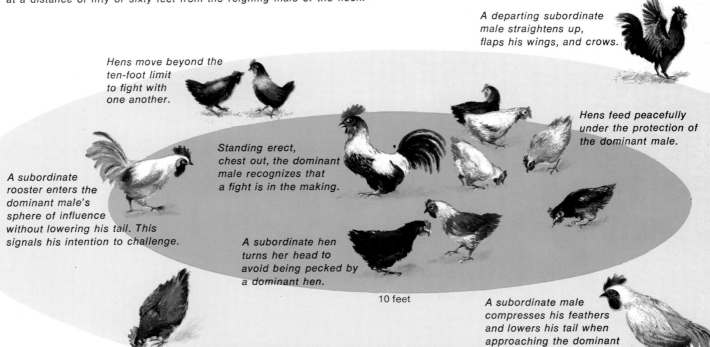

Hens move beyond the ten-foot limit to fight with one another.

A subordinate rooster enters the dominant male's sphere of influence without lowering his tail. This signals his intention to challenge.

Standing erect, chest out, the dominant male recognizes that a fight is in the making.

A subordinate hen turns her head to avoid being pecked by a dominant hen.

Hens feed peacefully under the protection of the dominant male.

A subordinate male compresses his feathers and lowers his tail when approaching the dominant rooster.

10 feet

20 feet

What seems to the untrained eye to be a noisy chaos, whether in the wild or in a chicken house, is actually an elaborate, shifting social scene in which the various dominant animals control the behavior of their nearby subordinates.

The human intruder into a chicken house who swings wide the door and clumps into the chickens' orderly society will send all the birds flying to the far end of the building. What follows is one of the most exhausting and trying of times in the life of a chicken. Suddenly crowded by other strange chickens, the dominant birds peck in all directions to regain their personal space. The stable, well-controlled social life imposed by the peck order is destroyed, and usually takes considerable time to rebuild.

In a large chicken house, where each animal recognizes only fifty or so other birds around it, there are actually a great number of flocks with overlapping memberships. It may take hours for each animal to find its original position among familiar neighbors.

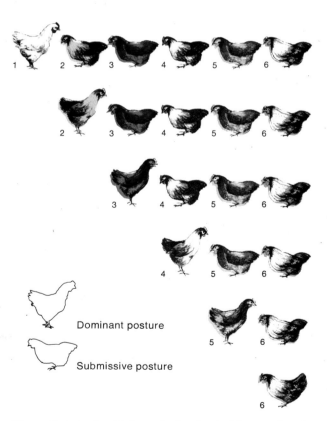

The peck order in chickens, in its simplest form, refers to the right of the highest ranking chicken to peck all the others. The second in rank behaves submissively to the first, but pecks those below it; and so on down the line.

A Universal Need

There is a tendency to smile when the animal is a chicken, but to a greater or lesser extent, most animals exhibit spacing behavior. In an experiment several tom turkeys were put together in a pen that was too small to satisfy their personal space requirements. Eventually the birds solved the problem by standing in a circle, all facing out. For turkeys, personal space is needed most in front of the face.

Human beings can appreciate the predicament of the crowded turkeys, for people, too, have a need for personal space. When someone comes too close to talk, the listener's immediate response is to back off. If the talker pursues, the uncomfortable listener continues to withdraw until stopped by a wall. Human beings are generally conscious of these rules only when broken.

If two friends are standing on a crowded bus, they usually carry on their conversation face to face about three feet apart. As the bus fills up with more people, they shift their positions so that they no longer face one another but are standing at an angle. Eventually they may touch, but shoulder to shoulder, never chin to chin.

The reverse works, too: as a crowded elevator empties out, the people left behind adjust their positions to gain more personal space. If an individual were left in the corner with only one other passenger, and that passenger continued to stand as close as before, the response might easily be one of alarm: "Is he some kind of nut?"

Animals are never conscious of breaches of personal space in an analytic way, as humans can be. They are simply aware of being crowded and act to regain the necessary space—by pecks, pokes, withdrawal, appeasement, vocal complaint, or whatever means is usual for their species.

This is not to say that all animals demand equal personal space. Some species are "contact" animals. With a whole beach to spread out on, walruses are commonly seen in great brown heaps, leaning all over one another, but never face to face. Their need for personal space is only in front, not to the side. Captive young walruses represent a danger to their keepers, for they greet a keeper with body-crushing enthusiasm. Some primates, too, are much inclined to body contact. Young bonnet macaques or social equals can be seen lounging against one another without any of the animals expressing the slightest objection. Lovebird pairs crowd together on a branch in apparent contentment. Parrots, titmice, and weaverbirds also have a strong tendency to clump.

Ring-billed gulls nest in large, noisy colonies that never seem to settle down. Each pair of birds defends a nesting territory, which involves constant squabbling with neighboring families. In the melee, chicks have a high mortality rate.

There is no such thing as security in the animal kingdom. Every victory is followed by another challenge

Animal societies are dynamic, shifting with the changing seasons and with the maturing of individuals. Just as the rearing of young brings territoriality in birds to its strongest expression, so the fledging of the young results in the breakup of paired birds and the abandonment of their territories.

In group-living animals, the attainment of maturity heralds the individual's drive to become part of the breeding population. Those animals that have dominance are challenged anew as every generation rises. There is always a youngster eager to claim his first territory or a dispossessed individual ready to challenge his neighbor. The have-nots make forays across the borders of the haves.

Exploration is a common feature of animal behavior. An animal on its own territory or home range is generally brisk and confident in its manner. Its behavior often changes dramatically when it steps outside these bounds. It becomes wary and will flee homeward at the slightest movement or sound. This tentativeness and readiness to flee is characteristic of animals on unfamiliar ground or on the territories of neighbors. A trespassing lion is easy to identify, for an individual off his land has none of the careless, proud demeanor that has earned for lions the title "King of Beasts."

Exploratory behavior is important to survival because an animal that has explored the region beyond its home has somewhere to run if flight back to its nest is prevented. The field mouse whose nest is overturned by a plow has probably surveyed the neighboring hedgerow; it can find cover at once. Exploration, the first step toward familiarity, is a life-and-death matter to such small rodents, which are preyed upon by everything from owls to cats. They must have knowledge

How a Redwing Blackbird Lost His Territory

Territorial defense may fail when a holder must fend off several challengers. Here, male redwing A was initially successful in keeping male B off his territory. Then males C and D arrived, and while A was driving off C, D took over a portion of the territory. Later A disappeared altogether, and B occupied the remainder of the territory. Meanwhile, C established a territory farther from the lake.

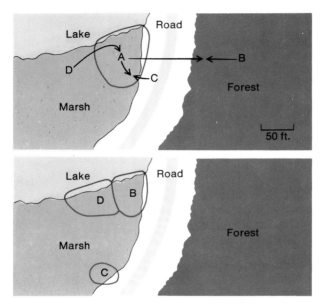

A male redwing blackbird proclaims ownership of a territory by singing and flashing his bright shoulder patches. After the breeding season, both the plumage and the aggression fade, and the birds gather in winter flocks.

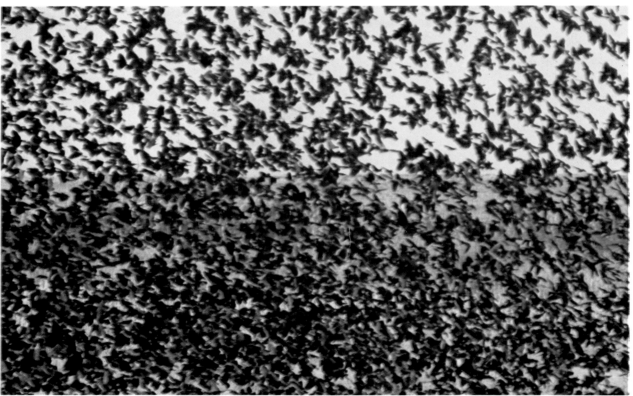

of a nearby hiding place at every moment of their lives, whenever they venture forth.

For other species, exploration is the means by which the landless young become territory owners. They tour the land looking for opportunities to settle. Generally, the owner of a territory—or a home-ranging animal on its own timetable—has the advantage when it meets such an explorer. The owner is familiar with all the features of the area. Its confidence may arise from success in defending its territory many times, or perhaps from a dim awareness on the part of a home-ranging animal that it is on its usual timetable and so has priority. But there is also a kind of "social inertia" on the part of the intruder, an acceptance of the owner's prior claim that seems to limit its effectiveness in a challenge.

In order to win, a challenger must be far more aggressive in invasion than the resident needs to be in defense. This is unlikely, for the intruder usually lacks both the necessary familiarity with the ground it is trying to claim, and a safe "home base" from which to operate.

But chance often plays a part in the lives of animals. In one case history of territorial defense, a male redwing blackbird lost his territory to a bystander when his defense against a challenger carried him too far from his boundaries once too often. The challenger also lost to the bystander, ultimately giving up the fight entirely and finding a territory elsewhere. Such a case, where a territory owner defeats a challenger and then is itself usurped, is not uncommon in nature.

No claim to space, no rise in dominance goes unchallenged for long; contenders are always close at hand when a territory owner or the dominant leader of a group weakens or dies. They may even have settled their ranks among themselves, so that one has a clear advantage when an opportunity presents itself.

An encounter between two hoary marmots develops into a boxing, biting match. One marmot had intruded onto the other's turf. Before either was seriously injured, the trespasser accepted defeat and ran, pursued only a short way by the victor.

When one animal meets another of a different species, it may pay no attention, fight, or run for its life

On the spur of a mountain and its associated valleys, a host of creatures is likely to be found—deer, pumas, marmots, ground squirrels, beavers, badgers, mice, an assortment of birds, reptiles, spiders, insects, and many more. Certain of these are on defended territories and others are more casual in their use of space. No patch of ground is the exclusive domain of a single species; the claims overlap and intersect in hundreds of ways. This is the mosaic of landholding. The pattern is repeated from seaside marsh to tropical forest, each with characteristic kinds of animals.

What can be seen in a particular habitat—one that has not been disturbed by man—is the consequence of myriad minor adjustments in the behavior of each species over countless generations of association with all the others. They are adapted to the presence of their fellow creatures, and all their feeding and social patterns are in rough balance.

The cardinal rule of landholding is that the resources of the area are not exhausted by overgrazing or overkilling. Animals are not conscious of establishing food preserves for themselves, nor do they defend food as such—their claim is always to space.

Each species has built into its behavior the tendency to claim an amount of space that will support its needs. Except in times of drought or flood, the land contains enough food for all because animals spaced out on territories and home ranges do not destroy their food supply.

Some creatures seem oblivious of one another. One bluebird will drive off bluebirds and a deermouse will repel deermice at its burrow, but the

An African rainforest may be inhabited by one or several species of closely related monkeys, the guenons. Because each species has a tendency to stay in a particular stratum in the tall forests, they seldom fight. Dianas prefer the upper layer, the high canopy, but may be seen in the middle story as well. The red-tailed monkey is a regular commuter, spending the day on the forest floor and climbing to the middle layer to sleep. A green monkey may encounter a red-tail, a mona may have dealings with a moustached monkey, but in general, guenons are "worlds apart."

A great black-backed gull jabs furiously at a skua caught in the act of attacking a gull chick. Where the two species nest near each other, each preys upon the eggs and young of the other, and fighting between the species is common.

bluebird and the deermouse tend to ignore one another. Pairs of songbirds such as warblers, chickadees, and vireos may occupy the same tree. Because their food is different, and they favor different levels, with the warblers low in the tree, chickadees in the middle story, and vireos usually in the topmost branches, there is little conflict. Puma and spider, garter snake and deer, beaver and praying mantis all coexist peacefully.

However, when two different species have similar nesting or food needs, there is keen competition, especially in times of scarcity. Then a "biological rank" may emerge, where one species seems to have an automatic advantage in the contest.

Sparrows often drive off house martins to claim their partly finished nests. At a feeding place in the woods, a wild turkey may move freely, but doves will give the turkey wide berth. Doves, in turn, are avoided by quail. The subordinate species keeps its distance from the dominant.

The highly specific habitat preferences of warblers allow many species to live peaceably within a single forest community. A blackburnian chooses the upper branches of an evergreen for its nest, and a black-throated green warbler the middle level. The redstart also selects the middle of a tree, but the tree is deciduous. A redstart's "downstairs" neighbor is the black-and-white warbler. The amount of sunlight and moisture also affects warbler territories. The yellow-throat claims wet, sunlit forest floor, and the oven-bird sets up housekeeping in dry, shaded places.

Rarely do such large, powerful carnivores as a bear and a cougar come so close to one another. But in midwinter, when food is scarce, the lure of a deer carcass proves so tempting that they choose rather to feed than to fight.

A pack of Cape hunting dogs converges on a young wildebeest. In their excitement, the hunting dogs make twittering sounds, which attract a hungry lion. Just as the dogs bring down their prey, the big cat races in and cheats them of

A cheetah, which has a lower rank than a lion, is often deprived of its prey by the arrival of the more powerful beast. The cheetah may be inclined to defend its kill, but soon gives up, for in any fight it certainly would lose.

When a pride of lions settles down to feast on the carcass of a wildebeest, hyenas often skulk nearby. Though a single lion may be forced to give way to several hyenas, the hyenas do not dare to challenge a pride. When the lions leave, the hyenas feed. If anything is left, the jackals have their turn. Hovering about, looking for any opportunity, the omnipresent vultures also try to claim a share.

Ranks of this kind are not universal. Two powerful predators such as a bear and a cougar have no automatic ranking system. Driven by hunger, and with no wish to fight one another, they may have an uneasy truce while both feed cautiously from opposite ends of a deer carcass.

In the prey-predator relationship, prey animals are eternally vigilant. The range of a predator always includes populations of plant feeders, otherwise there would be no food for the hunter. Mink in a marsh specialize in feeding on muskrats. The marten lives primarily on squirrels. These predators could not earn a living entirely in the immediate vicinity of their homes; they need an area large enough to feed their litters in the rearing season, after which the pattern of movement may change for the winter, and a different prey species may be taken.

their prize. The hunters stand aside reluctantly as the lion seizes the wildebeest, finally killing it with a neck bite.

The Flight Distance

All animals that avoid others, whether as prospective prey or because they have a lower biological rank, have a "flight distance"—an amount of space that they maintain between themselves and their enemies. On the African plains, where prey and predator are frequently within sight of one another, the rules are clear. Prey must be wary, but they do not run until the predator comes near. This behavior is an adaptation of individual species of animals, and is finely adjusted to the speed of the predator.

If a gazelle has sufficient warning, it can outrun a lion. The lion's strategy for catching it is surprise. It must come within the flight distance of the gazelle and begin its charge before the prospective meal has a chance to escape.

Pigeons in a city park have a particularly short flight distance. Watching a child trying to catch a pigeon is a study in this fine adjustment. The birds forage on the ground and take wing only when the child comes within a few feet.

What is known of flight distance is based in large measure on how near man can come before an animal flees, and this is conditioned by the animal's prior experience with human beings— whether it has been hunted or molested in any way. A giraffe may run when a man approaches on foot to within 150 yards; if the man is in a motor car, it takes off at twenty-five yards. Perhaps the man on foot, recognizable as some sort of creature, inspires fear sooner than the loud motor of a Land Rover. In large open parks, where the animals are protected and men on foot and in automobiles are commonplace, the giraffes flee not at all; they become used to man as a harmless presence in their midst.

The interrelationships of species living together are extremely complex, and few studies of these associations have yet been made. Consequently, many curious phenomena remain unexplained.

Why does the hyena that lives among its prey generally hunt away from its own den? In Norway, a pair of merlin falcons were observed nesting in an old crows' nest in the middle of a fieldfare colony. Merlins usually prey on these thrushes, and fieldfares generally mob a predator. But this pair of merlins entered and left the colony unmolested. It is not known whether such coexistence kept away other large predators, or if the fieldfares were sentries for the merlins.

There are myriad unexplained uses of space in the wild, many conditions controlling the behavior of animals that remain to be discovered.

The Race to Reproduce

To arrive first, call loudest, fight hardest, or perhaps
merely to flutter or stand still — animal courtship takes many forms.
Though all animals seek to reproduce, not all succeed

ChiChi, the only female giant panda outside communist China, has turned out to be a disappointment. She has rejected as a mate the only available male panda. She was flown to the Moscow zoo to meet her suitor, named AnAn, in the hope they would mate and produce offspring. But ChiChi would not cooperate. Later AnAn was brought to the London zoo with the idea that ChiChi might accept him on her own ground. This, too, failed.

The scientists and keepers who tried to bring about the mating of these appealing creatures introduced them to one another in stages, gave them seclusion, and finally, treated ChiChi with hormones to stimulate sexual behavior. Nothing overcame her resistance.

It may be that ChiChi and AnAn, one or both, were too old to mate. At approximately twelve years of age, they are approaching the record age for captive pandas. Perhaps, after so many years without seeing other pandas, ChiChi no longer recognizes AnAn as one of her own species; she is far friendlier with her keepers than with him. Or it is possible that AnAn's long years away from

Wide-open jaws signal attack when male hippos meet, but in courtship, male and female only play at fighting. They neither bite nor bellow. Other hippos, submerged out of the heat of a Uganda afternoon, do not interfere as the pair bobs gently in the river, "kissing" at full gape.

other pandas have changed his behavior in some way that makes him unacceptable to ChiChi.

This unfortunate state of affairs points up the fact that mating is never a simple matter of the meeting of an adult female and male of the same species. Mating occurs only when the time, the place, the behavior of the animals, their age, and many other factors are perfectly meshed.

Year after year, without any knowledge that there is a connection between mating and producing of offspring, most animals in the wild mate on a regular timetable. For each species, this guarantees that eggs will hatch or young will be born under the best possible conditions for survival.

Changes in the environment, and in their own bodies, stimulate animals to mate. Sunlight, temperature, and rainfall all influence an animal's internal condition, and there are as well self-sustained rhythms within each individual. The external world and these internal rhythms must be perfectly synchronized before the reproductive process can begin.

The sun, the supreme agent of change, is also the most reliable timepiece in nature. Warm weather or the first rains may be early or late, but the amount of sunlight each day increases or decreases seasonally with perfect regularity.

Thus the sun is the "clock" that sets the breeding behavior of many creatures. The gradual change of light—increasing in spring, decreasing in fall—is sensed and measured by the part of the

The male superb lyrebird's tail feathers begin to show in a short brush, poking downward. When fully developed, they are an incredible two feet long. The Australian bird courts by throwing his tail over his head, forming a lacy canopy.

brain called the hypothalamus. The hypothalamus responds by relaying the information to the master control gland of the body, the pituitary.

Now a steady sequence of changes in the body brings the animal into breeding condition. The pituitary gland releases hormones into the bloodstream. These powerful substances cause the sex glands—ovaries in females, testes in males—to increase in size and to secrete more sex hormones, which, in turn, influence the nervous system so that breeding behavior is activated.

The sights and sounds of courtship are recorded by the senses of the animal, and this further stimulates the hypothalamus, the pituitary, and the sex glands, in a smoothly escalating system.

As dawn comes earlier with the approach of spring, birds in winter flocks become restless, and take off for their breeding grounds. Males that have flocked together all winter often become aggressive, intolerant of other males of their species. They signal readiness to mate by establishing territories. The females, too, respond to internal changes, though often less obviously than males.

The physical changes in birds are seen most vividly in the beautiful nuptial plumage that appears in spring, usually just in the males. The male peacock's long, iridescent tail coverts are completely developed. The male scarlet tanager's drab coloration of winter, similar to the year-round plumage of the female, becomes bright red.

In most birds, mating is followed immediately by egg-laying, incubation, hatching, and caring for young. The sequence begun by changing daylength is continuous right up to the time the offspring become independent.

Many rodents and other small mammals have breeding cycles similar in length to those of birds —birth following soon after mating. But for large mammals, mating may occur many months before birth. The female American bison carries a developing embryo in her womb for nine months; for the spotted axis deer of Asia, this gestation period is about eight months.

Unlike birds and small mammals, these animals have no way of adapting their mating behavior to weather conditions or food supplies that will be available months later, when the young are born. Their mating schedules, established through countless generations, are based mainly on the survival of the greatest number of offspring. Their young inherit the tendency to mate at the same time of year as their parents did, and thus the pattern is fixed.

Mammals arrive at sexual readiness in the same way as birds—through changes in the hypothalamus, pituitary, and sex glands—but their bodily changes are less apparent. Mammals do not have the equivalent of nuptial plumage.

Hormonal changes bring the female mammal into a condition called estrus. This is a period, usually brief, when an egg is fully developed and ready to be fertilized. Estrus is signaled to males by the emission of scents that are given off for some time before the peak of estrus is reached;

Elk stags lock antlers, fighting to claim a harem. A fall breeding season is common among large mammals, whose young take many months to develop in the womb. Birth occurs the following spring, when the chance of surviving is greatest.

this guarantees that the male will be available when fertilization can occur.

Sexual interest wanes in both male and female as the scents and behavior of estrus subside. The male shrew can safely approach the female only during estrus. In the laboratory, female shrews have been known to kill males that were left in their cages beyond this time.

The Opportunists

Though daylength and temperature are powerful regulators of breeding in birds, rainfall is a decisive timing factor among desert birds. Several species of desert quail of the southwestern United States respond to changing daylength, but defer their breeding during a drought.

On the plains of Africa and in the dry outback of Australia, many species of birds are ready to engage in breeding whenever the rains come. As torrents move swiftly across the plains, they may wet an area only a few miles wide. In the wake of such a storm, it is common to find a narrow belt of flourishing vegetation. Birds on this strip are busily engaged in nesting, incubation, or feeding of young. A few miles away, where the rains did not touch, other birds of the same kind remain in non-breeding flocks.

The tiny locust finch of southeast Africa, the zebra finch of Australia, and many other finches follow this pattern. The zebra finch is remarkable because it begins courtship at once—in the pouring rain! Parakeets are also opportunistic.

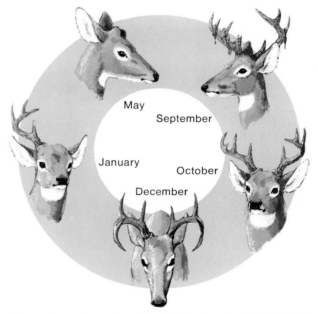

May
September
January
October
December

The antlers of a male white-tailed deer begin to grow in spring, showing first as mere bumps. Antlers are covered with velvet, a hairy skin well supplied with blood vessels and nerves. The velvet protects and provides nutrients for the growing bony structures. Because antlers are sensitive at this time, a deer avoids striking them against hard objects. By September, the antlers are fully grown and hardened. The velvet begins to dry out, and the deer rubs off the dead skin. As fall advances, decreasing daylength and colder weather stimulate the deer's endocrine system. The male's neck thickens, and he becomes aggressive toward other males. At the peak of the breeding season, in December, males use their antlers to fight for possession of females. Deer shed their adornments when the breeding season ends in January, or perhaps a month or so later.

Put into a cage with a female ring dove, the male bows and coos. He gives a distinctive nest call to announce selection of a nest site (the glass bowl).

The male brings materials as the female constructs the nest. The stimulation of this activity brings both birds to sexual readiness.

The first egg is usually laid eleven days after courtship begins. Incubation is shared, but the male generally sits only for six or so hours.

During the incubation period, the crop (a pouch in the gullet) begins to enlarge in both adults. It secretes crop milk, on which the young will feed.

Fourteen days after laying, the eggs hatch. The nestling ring dove plunges its head down a parent's throat, where it feeds directly from the crop.

Young ring doves can peck grain at two weeks and are rejected soon after. Rearing is complete, and their parents enter into a second, identical cycle.

The Ritualized Reproduction of Ring Doves

Ring doves require certain conditions in order to mate, build a nest, lay and incubate eggs, and rear young. At first the birds respond to the warmth and increasing day-length of spring, then to the presence and behavior of a prospective mate. There is a gradual escalation of the reproductive process, in which each event triggers the next. The bowing and cooing of the male cause the female's ovi-ducts to swell, increasing to five times their non-breeding size. If no male is present, egg-laying does not occur. The absence of nesting materials (a situation tested in the laboratory) also inhibits breeding behavior. The presentation of a nest with eggs already in it does not stimulate incubation. Each step is taken only when ring doves are physically and psychologically prepared for it.

The Social Whirl

Animals are profoundly affected not only by the physical environment, but also by the behavior of their own kind. Some birds and mammals do not mate unless many others of their species are present. In crowded seabird colonies, the pairs of birds courting in the close quarters of their small territories become excited by the calling and posturing of others around them.

The black-legged kittiwake, a gull, breeds on islands from northwest Alaska to the Aleutians as well as on the coast of Greenland and adjacent areas. When the population density of their colonies is high, mating behavior speeds up. The birds seem to be stimulated by seeing many others in the fervor of courtship. This tendency is called the Darling Effect, after the British biologist who identified it.

It may be that the lack of such mutual stimulation brought about the extinction of the American passenger pigeon. These birds lived in massive flocks of several million each. It is estimated that at least three billion passenger pigeons were living in North America at one time. As the country filled with settlers, the birds were killed off in huge numbers as wooded areas were cleared.

By the time voices rose to protest the killing of passenger pigeons, in all probability it was too late. These pigeons were adapted to mob existence. On winter roosts in southern swamps, the myriads of birds perched on every available branch, packed side by side in a noisy mass. Their nestings in northern forests were likewise crowded, often covering fifty square miles or more. The female laid only one egg a year, but even at such a low reproductive rate, the passenger pigeon was phenomenally successful.

The swarming millions of pigeons were also incredibly destructive. The nesting area was left in a shambles of broken branches, despoiled vegetation, and a deep carpet of bird dung. Since the pigeons despoiled a roost or nesting place in one season, they moved on to others, never returning to a site until the land had recovered.

As the nestings were broken up and birds were wantonly slaughtered for the market, their numbers declined steeply. Then all at once they were gone. There are no small flocks of passenger pigeons in an inaccessible valley somewhere in North America. They died out, probably because they could not breed in small colonies. The rowdy, ear-splitting masses of fellow pigeons appear to have been an essential to successful breeding.

Thousands of elegant terns call raucously, quarreling over nest sites on Raza Island, off the Gulf of California. The birds only begin courting in earnest after the colony has been brought to fever pitch by mass excitement.

Synchronized Births

When rams enter a flock of domestic sheep, they stimulate and synchronize the estrus cycle of the ewes. Studies have shown that when the males are introduced into the grazing area in late summer, usually none or few of the ewes are in estrus. Seventeen days after the rams appear, the ewes come into estrus, all at the same time. The ewes that do not come into estrus then will do so in another eighteen days—or one cycle later.

Buffalo, deer, and antelope males and females usually live apart except at the mating season, when the arrival of the males also appears to synchronize estrus in the females.

The survival value of closely timed mating within a group is that most of the births occur within a short period. On the plains of Africa, as the time of birth arrives, the predators—lions, hyenas, baboons, leopards, and hunting dogs—circle the herds of zebras and antelopes. These predators are efficient hunters, and the countless young are especially vulnerable.

For a short time, until the young are strong and fleet of foot, the predators have a relatively easy time of it. But prey animals generally kill only what they can eat, and they need only so much food at one time. The herds lose far fewer young than they would if the calves were born over a

The light-coated calves in a herd of wildebeest are highly attractive to enemies. Calves can run with the herd, but are easily overtaken. The presence of many youngsters—more than predators need for food—ensures that some survive.

longer period. As they mature and are better able to escape the leopard's claws, the feasting becomes more difficult. The predators go back to the harder work of hunting older animals.

Colonial nesting birds have the same advantage. The losses to meat-eaters are necessarily great, but are limited by the fox's or the cat's appetite. Within these colonies, there is the additional advantage of many eyes alert for the predator's approach. When disturbed, the birds swoop down and attack.

The Fabulous Voyagers

Nowhere is the prelude to breeding more spectacular than among migratory birds. The first stage in their breeding cycle is the journey to their traditional nesting grounds. The more that is learned about migration, the more astonishing it seems. Built into the animals' brains is the ability to use the sun or the stars as a compass. Guided by celestial light, the arctic terns migrate from wintering grounds in the southern Atlantic, Pacific, and Indian oceans to breeding areas half a world away, on the northern coasts of North America, Europe, and Asia.

There are many theories about how birds developed migration routes, mainly connected with the effect the Ice Ages had on their behavior. The history of migration will probably always be in the realm of speculation. There is, however, an advantage to nesting in an area where the days are long, in the high latitudes. By working through the many hours of daylight, the parent birds are able to bring their young to the fledgling stage earlier than in temperate regions.

This fact was revealed by a study of two different breeding groups of American robins. One group nested in Alaska, the other in Ohio. Both groups fed their nestlings about once every ten minutes. The Ohio robins fed their young for sixteen hours a day, for an average of 96 feedings. The Alaska robins fed their young for twenty-one hours, for an average of 137 feedings. The Ohio nestlings took wing at the age of thirteen days, the Alaska nestlings fledged at nine days.

The advantage of early fledging is great, for young in the nest are particularly vulnerable to predators. The sooner a young bird can fly, the better its chances for survival.

The migration of some birds is extraordinarily regular. Every year, at the end of the first week in October, the wedge-tailed shearwaters arrive at the coral beaches of the Great Barrier Reef off the coast of Australia. Millions come all the way from

A flight of greater snow geese *cuts across the sunset sky above Assateague Island National Seashore in Maryland. Each spring, these geese migrate hundreds of miles to breeding grounds on Greenland and on Baffin and Ellesmere islands.*

Siberia, stopping only briefly to feed and rest. The largest number arrive on the same day.

For the shearwater, also called the muttonbird, timing is all-important. The bird must compete for the prize that determines whether it will breed or not. Each pair must claim and defend a nesting burrow in the coral sand. The latecomers will find all the nesting sites occupied—there are never enough to go around. They will have lost what is, indeed, a race to reproduce.

Territorial squabbles and assertions of dominance reach their highest pitch right at the start of the breeding season. Each bird that claims space must fight to keep it. Only one pair of muttonbirds can occupy a burrow; no intruder can be allowed to enter, for this would jeopardize the survival of the young. The quarrels between the haves and the have-nots must be settled before the young arrive. Thereafter, the owners of the burrow continue to defend, but the conflict subsides because the have-nots quit trying to oust them.

Ownership of a territory often determines whether a bird can attract a mate. Usually it is the male who sets up housekeeping, and the females select from among the territory-holders. This system sometimes leads to fights among females. The Adélie penguin male may stand on his little territory while two females call excitedly and beat one another with their flippers. The male takes no part in the fray—he is simply the prize. It is only after one female has driven off the other that courtship between the male and female can begin.

Two species of seabird, kittiwakes and murres, claim space on this Icelandic cliff. The cries of many murres, protesting new arrivals, sound like a growling chorus. But the homesteading does not stop until every shelf is filled.

Finding a Mate

Animals probably never know what they themselves look like. There are no mirrors in nature to establish in the animal's mind that it is a bear or a robin. The glassy surface of a lake does not seem to perform this function. In fact, when an animal looks in a mirror, it may threaten the opposing image, attack it, or even court it.

But with few exceptions, animals mate with their own kind. How do they know that a particular animal is a suitable mate? Failure of an animal to recognize one of its own species may lead to biologically useless matings that produce no young. Or, if the mating does result in the birth of hybrid young, the offspring may be sterile. The mule, offspring of a female horse and a male donkey, is a strong, useful farm animal, but it is a biological dead end.

Crossbreeding is often practiced in the management of domestic animals, but it is seldom successful in the wild because the hybrid animal is rarely able to find a mate from either of its parents' species. Among gulls, for example, where populations of two or more different species use adjacent or overlapping breeding grounds, crossbreeding is exceptional, even though the species look alike superficially.

The female gull is the one who does the choosing of a mate. The decisive factors in her choice are subtle differences in the pattern of the eye—the color contrast of the fleshy ring around the eye and iris. In almost every case, she will select a mate exactly like herself, probably because the male is like her parents—both of whom she would normally resemble.

Probably the pattern of plumage also aids the gulls in identification—it varies slightly in every species. And vocal differences play a part. But detection by eye pattern seems to predominate.

The value of such reproductive isolation may well be to preserve the adaptations the species has made to an environment. Tolerance to temperature, resistance to disease, or ability to take advantage of certain kinds of food are passed on to the offspring.

Whatever the reasons, the fact is that most animals are strongly attracted only to their own kind. Indeed, even when animals are reared by the wrong parents, by accident or by experiment, a large percentage will revert to the ancestral behavior pattern the following year—even though they may have mated successfully with an individual of the foster parents' species the first time.

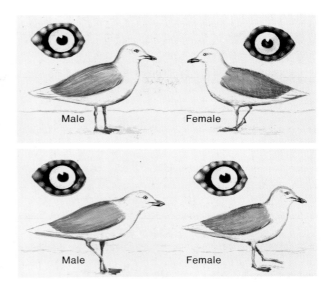

The "Right" Appearance

To find out how gulls identify potential mates, scientists used a harmless paint to make the eye-rings of one species look like those of a different species. When a female's eye-ring was changed, she was still able to win a mate, but a male with the wrong markings could not. This indicates that female gulls, not males, select partners. If the rings are changed after pairing, however, a female will remain with an "alien" mate, but a male will depart.

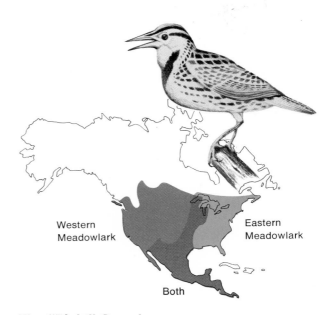

Western Meadowlark

Eastern Meadowlark

Both

The "Right" Sound

Western and eastern meadowlarks are remarkably similar in appearance, yet in the region where their ranges overlap, the two do not interbreed. Birds are able to detect miniscule differences in feature, but it was discovered that this is not what keeps the meadowlark species apart. Each has a distinctive call note that allows the birds to recognize whether another bird is an appropriate mate.

Courtship often begins in fear. The approach of another animal, even a suitable mate, seems threatening at first

Courting may begin between closely resembling species, but somewhere along the line, a wrong signal is given. The would-be mates then cease their attempts to form a bond. For courtship is actually an elaborate signaling system, remarkably diverse in its manifestations, whereby individuals communicate with potential mates.

Courtship among birds often starts off with behavior that looks like warfare. The male bank swallow takes up a territory and drives out all intruders, even females. At first he does not seem to recognize the difference between the sexes. But the female bank swallow is persistent and returns repeatedly in the face of his attacks, until finally he accepts her. The birds then form a pair bond and defend their territory against all comers.

The special attachment of the pair bond is formed in many ways. In bank swallows, the male's resistance must be overcome; in other species, such as the great crested grebe, the sexes seem to be equally uneasy about the approach of the opposite sex.

By its very nature, the formation of a bond involves an invasion of personal space or territory. This is a real barrier that must be broken down so male and female can come together. Courtship includes an approach ceremony, which may be either threatening or appeasing. But to form a bond there must also be behavior that binds, and to mate there must be behavior that stimulates.

From an English hedgerow, a bright-breasted male yellowhammer sings. A drab-colored female visits; then by adopting a threatening posture, she drives the male away. Should he resist, there may be a brief fight. But he makes no attempt to drive her from his territory as he would another male. She may stay and feed and then fly off. Over the next few days, she may visit a number of males, repeating her courtship sequence with each. Finally she selects a particular male by staying with him longer each visit, and by discontinuing her visits to other males.

An "engagement" period follows in which the pair of yellowhammers build up a daily routine. They feed and explore the area together, calling and tail-flicking back and forth, becoming used to

Courtship of the Great Crested Grebe

Few birds can match the great crested grebe in the variety or vigor of its courtship. Every element in its elaborate plumage—from ornamental tufts on the head to its rather insignificant tail—is employed in display. Initially, the male and female are hostile and fearful. Indeed, their courtship postures, expressing interest, appeasement, and excitement, are taken from the bird's repertoire of aggressive and defensive behavior. Male and female roles are interchangeable, though the female seems to be the one that advertises for a mate. She attracts attention with a series of croaking, far-reaching calls. If a possible mate responds, either sex may begin head-shaking, or perform any of their other courtship rituals. These grebes, which nest in fresh water from Scandinavia to New Zealand, cooperate in rearing young. Displaying continues throughout this time, enhancing their bond.

The most common courtship gesture is head-shaking. Each bird swivels its head rapidly four or five times in what looks like an emphatic "no, no."

Head-shaking may be followed with a quick preening of the wing feathers.

In one of the most intricate displays, a grebe dives, then rises erect out of the water in front of its partner. The other bird crouches in a "cat" posture.

being close. For a short time the male may bring nesting material, which is part of his later sexual behavior. But he interrupts this ceremony and begins chasing the female furiously through their territory until exhausted.

The second stage of courtship does not begin until May, more than two months after their first encounter. The male yellowhammer finds a twig and runs with it in his beak to dense cover. With lowered head, level back, and quivering wings, he shows his mate the nesting site he has selected. Unaided by the male, the female sometimes begins building her nest there. As she builds, the male displays to her. Repeatedly, he approaches the female, then turns and runs away with feathers fluffed as though frightened. At the end of his short run, he may pick up some nesting material, but this seems to be purely symbolic.

From time to time, the male yellowhammer turns and runs toward the female with his bill and wings raised. The female responds to one of these runs by crouching in the mating posture, which is like the food-begging attitude of fledglings. The male hops on to her back and mating follows. The female yellowhammer is aggressive in her behavior, and the male's approach to mating is timid, but from this time on she never attacks him. Gradually, his mating approach becomes more confident and less ceremonious.

The elements of yellowhammer courtship are common to many birds: One sex, usually the male, boldly imposes itself on the other and establishes dominance. The pair is conditioned to the presence of each other through a round of joint activities; there may be a chase scene, and the offering of gifts. Throughout the whole routine, the behavior of the male and female is reciprocal. There is an appropriate response to each action, depending on the species of bird.

In wild chickens, the rooster picks up a gift tidbit and clucks for the attention of his females. As they gather round, he drops it in front of one of them. Then he threatens her, she crouches, and they mate. He also picks nesting sites, one after another. The hen follows him around examining each in turn, sometimes going back to the first.

One or another element of courtship may have more importance to a species—a drake, for instance, does not have nest-showing in his repertoire—but whatever the set rituals, they are faithfully followed. Any failure to make a "right move" thwarts the appropriate behavior in the other member of the pair, and if not rectified could lead to breakup.

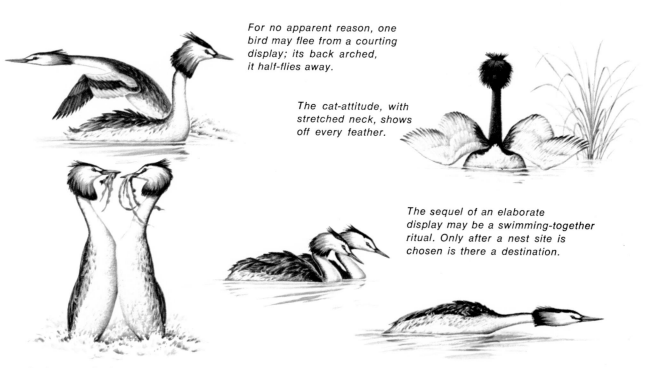

For no apparent reason, one bird may flee from a courting display; its back arched, it half-flies away.

The cat-attitude, with stretched neck, shows off every feather.

The sequel of an elaborate display may be a swimming-together ritual. Only after a nest site is chosen is there a destination.

In the penguin dance, two grebes dive for weeds, then rise abruptly out of the water. As they tread water, their breasts touch.

The neck-forward posture, used in courtship, is of great significance when the birds have paired; it is an invitation to mate.

Like all members of the cat family, the male and female lion court rather noisily. In what looks like a case of mixed feelings, they snarl, hiss, and swat a bit—but there is no real hostility. The female, a member of the male's pride, is approached for mating only when in breeding condition. This is signaled by the emission of scents.

Mammal courtship is usually brief, for male and female rarely form an enduring bond or cooperate in rearing young

Some mammals such as wolves and gibbons form pairs. Their pair-bonding behavior is of the longest duration of all species. Once formed, the bond is in effect year round, sometimes for life. Monkeys that do not form pairs, but which live in troops throughout the year, are also familiar with one another, and although there may be some personal resistance to be overcome, the preliminaries to mating are usually quite brief.

In a troop of baboons, a female in season attracts males with her sexual skin—the red area around her rump, which begins to swell and provides a visual signal. She mates first with subordinate males. The most dominant males become interested only at the peak of her estrus, when the sexual skin is fully developed. Thus a dominant male is most likely to sire her young. As her estrus subsides, she may resume mating with subordinate males—dominate males lose interest.

Among solitary species, the parents rarely form bonds, and the female rears her young unaided. Opossums, weasels, and raccoons meet, mate, and then separate. This is not to say that the males and females of these species are total strangers. Several females commonly live within the males' home ranges, and all the animals of the region will have a certain acquaintanceship with others of their species. But courtship does not build a bond; it leads only to mating.

When the female mammal emits the scents of estrus, more than one male may approach. Fights between rival males are quite common. The vanquished animal leaves the scene to the victor, who begins the courtship ritual of his species.

The hamster enters a female's territory and marks various places with his scent. This practice,

The raised head, open mouth, and wrinkled nose of a male impala indicate his intention to mate. The female expresses sexual readiness by simply standing still.

A "tending pair" of bison mates on the plains of Montana. Females with calves are joined by males in June; mating occurs from mid-July to August; males depart in September.

which is widespread among mammals, may be a response to a strange area. More probably, it is a means of familiarizing the female with the male's scent. The female flees from him in a formal sexual chase. As he follows, the male gives a call similar to the distress call of an infant hamster. This appears to attract and appease the female, and she allows his approach. Then he follows her into her burrow and they mate.

Male pronghorns live through the dry season apart from the females. When the rains begin, the males migrate into the female areas. Each male attempts to round up a harem of females, and there are many contests among the males. Often the fight carries two males well away from the females, and the females are taken over by a third male not involved in the fray.

There is no bond between male and female in species such as these, and the females seem indifferent as to which male wins them. Nevertheless, as the harem of a bison or a water buffalo becomes established, the females compete to en-

ter the wallow he has created in the mud. The wallow appears to carry the scent of the bull.

A month or two after a water buffalo harem has been formed, the females give birth to their calves —the products of last year's mating. The females are aggressive toward the male at the time of birth, but a month later come into estrus and begin to accept his advances.

The male water buffalo adopts a characteristic posture, neck outstretched, head raised, and mouth and nose wrinkled. This posture is also seen in domestic cattle and other hoofed and horned animals. The male rubs his neck along the female's back. If she is not fully into estrus, she moves away. But if she is receptive, she stands still and is mounted.

After all the females have been mated, the male gradually loses interest and moves off. His place may be taken by a younger bull without a harem. But eventually all the males retire to their separate ranges, leaving the females to rear the calves.

In relaxed moments, animals spend much of

Borrowed Behavior

Courting animals often "borrow" the behavior of infants. The fluttering wing of a red avadat is much like that of a young bird soliciting its parents for food. As a courting male hamster pursues a female, he squeaks like an infant in distress. The response to such infantile behavior is an immediate lessening of fear, for an infant does not represent a threat to an adult.

their time caring for their bodies. Mammal parents often groom their young by licking, and birds groom their chicks by preening their feathers. It is not surprising to find that such behavior is used in situations such as courtship in which animals must overcome the tensions of close approach. The male bison grooms the female by licking; the cormorant male gently preens the head and neck feathers of his mate during courtship, and she often responds by doing the same. Mutual preening continues among many colonial-nesting water birds throughout their period of attachment.

Grooming is of great importance among cats. Before she is ready to mate, a female cat will repulse a courting male by vigorous attacks. The male is generally inhibited from biting the female, but she feels no such restraint. So courtship is fraught with danger to the male. Nevertheless, he continues to approach until he is allowed to lick her head. This has a quieting effect, and mating can proceed. After mating, the female may turn and strike out, forcing a rapid separation.

Few activities are more stimulating and lower tensions more effectively than play. Animals give clear signals that indicate their intention and readiness to play. Every dog owner can recognize at once when the dog is inviting its master to join in a romp. After such a play signal has been given, animals are able to approach one another without hostility or tension.

A playful approach is part of the courtship behavior of many species. For the social life of animals is full of occasions where behavior is borrowed from one situation and used effectively for a different function. In this case, the play of infancy is employed for courtship.

As they come into estrus, female otters and some seals frolic around the males, nipping them on the neck. The male meerkat, an African relative of the mongoose, approaches the female and engages her in a bout of play fighting. Sexual excitement increases until the male seizes the female by a fold of skin on her neck. She becomes still and he mates with her. The play fighting of male and female hippopotamuses takes the form of mock biting and chasing in the water.

Tokens and Tidbits

Another ritual of approach, common among birds, is the offering of a gift. This is a form of appeasement, and the object passed from one member of the pair to the other may be food, nesting materials, or even a colored petal.

Courtship feeding is another instance of borrowed behavior, derived from the parental feeding of young. It always involves close approach. A gull may use a food-begging posture to get close to its mate. Both assume this posture before mating. Courtship between a male and female pigeon begins with bowing and cooing display by the male, who puffs up the iridescent feathers on his neck. Both throw back their heads in a symbolic preening gesture, then the female responds with a food-begging posture, back flattened and head thrown back. The male opens his bill and she feeds from his crop. Withdrawing her bill, the female flattens her body again in the soliciting, or mating, posture. Thereupon the male flutters above her and they mate.

Early in the breeding season, a male screech owl finds a nest hole. He calls and flies to the hole repeatedly until he attracts a receptive female. The common tern female accepts the fish offered to her by her suitor, but she does not eat it. Hunger is not a factor in these courtship rites. A European robin may pause beside her mate and beg for food, even though her mouth may be filled with

The token presentation of nesting materials, which is part of gannet courtship, continues when the pair builds a nest. One bird guards the nest site against thieving neighbors while its mate collects seaweed and shoreline debris.

grubs. This courtship feeding helps to maintain the bond between male and female until the pair breaks up at the end of the breeding season. Courting is an everyday event, not just a prelude to mating.

Courtship feeding may take a practical turn, however. For many species—particularly birds of prey—the duties of incubation are exclusively female. "Glued" to her nest, a female makes a poor hunter; she can only catch what comes near her. In the cold of a spring evening, her eggs would quickly chill if she left them. The male is a good provider and brings her a share of his prey. When the young hatch and both parents hunt, the male continues to bring food, but only to his mate. She must tear it into pieces to feed their nestlings.

For other species of birds, the gift may be "something for the home." Nest materials are presented in the courtship of grebes, but this is mainly symbolic, since these materials are not used when the nest is actually built. The woodpecker male, on the other hand, excavates about 90 per cent of the nest cavity.

To an Adélie penguin, home is nothing more than a collection of pebbles. The bleak Antarctic shore on which these birds nest is strewn with many small stones, but the penguins are highly selective about the pebbles they choose. A penguin will bypass scores until it finds one that suits it (though the selected pebbles seem to an observer in no way different from others scattered around).

When the female Adélie approaches the male on his territory, the two will bow formally to one another. The female may move away and pick up a stone, which she drops on the male's territory. Or the male may allow the female onto the site and may place a stone there himself. Soon the two are engaged in hunting pebbles for the nest. The most desirable pebbles seem to be those belonging to another penguin, and pebble-stealing—and defense—can be seen throughout the milling colony. It was once believed that the male alone presented pebbles; in fact, both sexes sometimes bring the gift of a pebble when returning to the nest, even after the chicks are hatched.

Parades and Displays

An eye for color—perhaps even for beauty—brings a flourish to many courtship rituals among birds and fish. Extravagant nuptial finery comes in every hue, sometimes burnished with eye-catching iridescence of feather or scale. The superb blue wren is a brilliant blue and black bird of the Australian bushlands. The male's plumage is, indeed, superb, but he embellishes his display by offering a bright yellow flower or petal to his mate. This presentation continues irregularly throughout the breeding season.

Where colorful plumage is lacking, color may still be of importance in courtship. Among the bowerbirds of New Guinea and Australia, it is a general rule that the duller the male's plumage, the more elaborate his bower is likely to be.

Different species build their bowers either as huge, hutlike maypoles, large arenas, or "avenues," where every leaf and twig has been scrupulously removed. The avenue-builder clears or tamps down an area of the forest floor and erects two parallel walls of sticks, which he pokes firmly into the ground. These walls may meet overhead in an arch. The satin bowerbird even daubs his bower with charcoal mixed with saliva.

The male's finishing touch is the decoration of the bower entrance with colorful berries, shells, shiny stones, and bright feathers. Since the arrival of Western man, with his sloppy habit of dropping things, the bowerbird's display inventory has increased phenomenally. To the old list has been added any amount of colored paper, tinsel, buttons, broken glass, tin cups, plastic toys, bottle caps, coins, and electric cords.

A female satin bowerbird, in pale green plumage, enters the newly erected, undecorated bower of a male. When the bower is complete, it will be littered with bright blue objects, ranging from parrot feathers to bottle caps.

Many hawks, eagles, and falcons perform aerial maneuvers of breathtaking grace and precision as part of courtship. When red-tailed hawks display, the male flies above and slightly behind the female on a level course. As the male swoops downward, the female continues level. Just as the male's wings spread to diminish speed, the female rolls over, and their talons touch for an instant. They part as the male flies upward and the female rights herself.

Some bowerbirds display their treasure trove in neat piles, while other species tend to scatter their possessions indiscriminately. The male stays within his bower and calls to attract a female. Presumably dazzled by his "shop window," the female allows herself to be led into the bower to mate with him. She soon leaves to build her nest elsewhere. Before long her place is taken by another visiting female.

Elaborate courtship ceremonies are also found among fish, though family life is rare. Most fish simply spawn and leave their eggs to drift. The tilapia, a fish of the freshwater lakes of Africa, combines a courtship ritual and a family life of sorts. The male takes up a territory on the lake bed. He excavates a courtship cavity by shoveling away the sand and stones with his mouth. Hovering over the hollow with his body directed downward, he attracts a female. If she responds, he leads her to the cavity, swimming across it with his tail vibrating gently. Together they enter the mating cavity, circling one another.

As she spawns, the female tilapia retrieves her eggs into her mouth. The male swims by as she does this, waving his fins at her. The lower fins, which have small, egg-sized circles on them, cause the female to try to collect these "eggs" as well. The deceptive markings on the male's fins ensure that the female's eggs are fertilized, for he discharges sperm as she approaches.

Insect societies—which are all actually large families from single sets of parents—also have courtship rituals. A hive of honeybees cannot exist without a queen, nor a queen without a hive of worker bees. When a queen dies, after a lifetime of laying eggs, the workers feed several of the larvae on a glandular secretion from the workers' heads called royal jelly. Any female larva is potentially a queen if fed this substance for the duration of its larval stage. In preparation for the development of a queen, the worker bees place each selected larva in a large cell within the hive. When the new queens hatch, they meet and fight. One kills all the others. Now she is ready for her nuptial flight. Pursued by male bees, called drones, the queen leaves the hive. The most vigorous of the drones mate with the queen. From a single nuptial flight comes a new generation.

The courtship dance of the crowned crane—with its quick-steps, leaps, bows, and erect posturing—is performed to the accompaniment of loud cries. In swampy regions, the African birds may also decorate their backs with mud.

Privacy, Please

During mating, animals are quite defenseless from the attack of a predator or a rival who has been stimulated by the courtship displays. Freedom from interference is of great importance at this time. On a well-defended territory, there are no difficulties about dealing with others of the same species.

A harem bull, whether elephant seal or American elk, has driven away all contenders. Within a troop of chacma baboons, the male moves to the periphery of the group and forms a consort pair with a female in estrus. When ducks arrive at the breeding grounds in spring, the migratory flock breaks up. Courtship takes place in small groups, then the pairs go off, finding some shelter and seclusion before mating occurs.

But privacy is almost impossible for some animals. For the sage grouse, which has been observed at its traditional courting arenas, attack during mating is an ever-present danger. Groups of males aggregate in one area, each male claiming a relatively small territory. At dawn and dusk, the males fight and attract females by displays of their magnificent plumage and by making "plopping" sounds with their vocal sacs. This collection of males, all close together on small territories, is called a lek. It is believed that the concentration of males calling and displaying may be necessary to stimulate the females to sexual readiness.

A male sage grouse, his head buried by luxuriant plumage and inflated air sacs, "booms" to attract a mate. Several hundred males may gather in a courting arena on the North American prairie. Arrival of a female sets off vigorous displays.

The female sage grouse live in home ranges around the lek, and when ready to lay eggs, come to the lek to be mated. The arrival of a female sets off a frenzied response in the males. They simultanously threaten one another and court the female by displaying. As she crosses a territorial boundary, the resident in full array follows her in a zigzag course, during which he threatens each neighboring male.

Finally the grouse male circles in front of her. If she crouches, he mates with her. Sometimes the neighbors cross the boundaries of his territory to attack him. But the mating is brief, and he turns instantly to threaten them.

A hen grouse may cross several territories before mating, with the joint threat-courtship ceremony repeated on each. It is clear that some males are dominant, for most of the matings are carried out by only two or three of the dozen or more males generally present. Male prairie chickens and blackcocks—both resplendent of plumage—have similar arenas.

Building a Nest

Some birds mate before the nest is built, others while it is under construction. Either way, the nest must be finished by the time the female lays her eggs. Then the pageantry of courtship gives way to more secretive behavior, for the incubating bird is vulnerable to predators while on the nest, and the eggs themselves must be protected from pilfering enemies.

For birds that live in dense woodland, finding seclusion is fairly easy. Nests are commonly built in inconspicuous places. A human being may wander through a woodland that is alive with the sounds of birds and rarely see a nest.

Few nests are as conspicuous as those of some eagles, which build immense structures in tall trees or on cliffs, adding to them year after year. Their inaccessibility and the aggressive nature of the birds are a guarantee of privacy.

The variety of birds' nests ranges from none at all in the case of the fairy tern, which parks its eggs in the fork of a tree, to the elaborately woven colonial nests of the African weaverbirds.

The woodpecker's nest hole in the trunk of a tree is frequently taken over in subsequent years by birds of other species, while the original owner chisels out a new one elsewhere.

While ospreys and eagles put a new layer of material on the old site each season, most other birds build anew each year. Old nests of leaves and grass vanish, buffeted by wind and rain.

Camouflage depends on where the species lives. The blacksmith plover of Africa, itself conspicuous, effectively hides its eggs in zebra dung. A related species, the Eurasian golden plover, nests in the foliage-carpeted tundra of the North, where its speckled plumage serves to conceal it.

The bulbous nests of black-headed weaverbirds droop like so many Christmas ornaments from a clump of trees in Kenya. The nests of these birds, woven of plant fibers, are just one of many types of weaverbird nest. Another species, the sociable weaverbird, lives in groups of as many as 300 individuals in immense, thatched, communal dwellings.

A Sanctuary for the Young

Though the function of nests is always to provide protection for the young, there is great variety in nest construction. Some species, such as quail, assemble a vague arrangement of grasses, which is abandoned as soon as the young hatch. For others, nest construction is a major undertaking; the nest serves as a cradle for the young until they are ready for independence. Birds exhibit amazing ingenuity in making use of local materials for housing.

Flicker   Nuthatch   Chickadee   Bluebird   Tree swallow   Starling

Many nests, especially those in tree holes, have a succession of tenants. The flicker, a kind of woodpecker, may chop out the hole. In later years, others take over, each making adjustments to suit its needs—perhaps enlarging the entrance, or building a nest within it. Starlings are often last, for they leave it in a filthy condition.

The fairy penquin of Australia and New Zealand, smallest of all penguins, is unusual because it nests in deep burrows rather than in plain view in a rookery.

The flask-shaped mud nests of cliff swallows, built side by side, look like a tenement. The birds usually build in a sheltered place, but the nests are often damaged by rain and must be repaired or rebuilt entirely.

An osprey nest, protected by a "moat," is conspicuous but inaccessible to most predators. This fish-feeding species is dying out. Pesticides have impaired development of the egg shells, which crack when incubated.

Bills touching, a pair of black-headed gulls mates. Their stormy courtship, which begins with a hostile jabbing of beaks, gradually becomes more peaceful as the birds wave their heads appeasingly, and perform aerial displays.

The culmination of courtship is mating. An egg is fertilized and a new life begins

When mating occurs, the sperm of the male enters the female's reproductive tract. At the uppermost part of this tract, the sperm comes in contact with the female's ovum. This cell is one of the largest cells found in nature, the part of a bird's egg that is usually called the yolk. The genetic material of the ovum, which is just below the surface, is the same size as the hereditary material from the sperm.

These two microscopic bits of life join to form a complete nucleus, the starting point of a new individual. This cell divides into two, then four, eight, sixteen, thirty-two, and so on.

As the yolk travels down the oviduct—literally,

the duct for the egg—the cells continue to divide. The yolk is a food reserve for the growing embryo, made up of about half protein and fats, and half water. As the yolk passes along, a coating of albumen, or egg white, is secreted around it from the walls of the oviduct.

The albumen also contains protein, but it is 90 per cent water, which cushions the delicate embryo against damaging shocks in the early stages, and later supplies water to the growing embryo.

Farther down the oviduct, a shell membrane is secreted. The albumen has great water-retention capabilities, which cause it to swell against the membrane, thus providing a firm surface on which the shell can form. The formation of the hard outer shell is the last stage, and the longest in the sequence. In chickens, it takes a little more than sixteen hours for the shell to form.

Inside the egg, cell divisions continue, but not to any extent until incubating begins. Hundreds,

From Ovum to Shell

A fertilized ovum, with a supply of yolk, travels down the oviduct. The walls of this muscular tube secrete albumen. Farther along, membranes are added. The albumen swells within the membranes, providing a firm base on which the shell forms. The entire process takes about twenty-four hours.

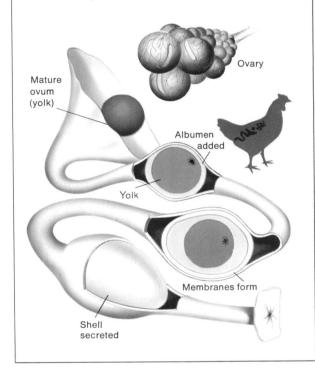

Ovary

Mature ovum (yolk)

Albumen added

Yolk

Membranes form

Shell secreted

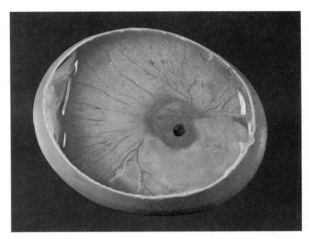

At two days, the circulatory system in a chicken's egg is well established, and heart pulsations can be detected in the embryo. The head may be identified by the large eye.

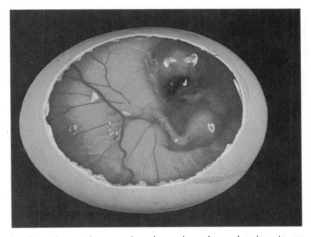

At five days, the much-enlarged embryo begins to resemble a bird, as its limbs become more prominent. It already has the beginnings of a beak, tongue, and intestines.

At twenty days, the chick has attained maximum growth within the shell—there is no more room, and the food supply is exhausted. In another day, it will begin to hatch.

and thousands, then ultimately millions of cells develop, organizing themselves by stages into the different tissues of the body. A network of blood vessels forms, infiltrating the yolk.

The efficiency of the egg is truly amazing. A remarkable system of suspended membranes and a water cushion protect the embryo from shock. The shell is a porous structure, but the membranes and albumen prevent excessive evaporation. They also provide a barrier to disease organisms. At hatching, the chick has used up almost all the food and water, and emerges ready to continue its growth in the outside world.

The degree of development of a chick at hatching is determined by the amount of yolk in the egg. In songbirds, the yolk occupies only about a fifth of the egg's total volume. The chick hatches out blind, naked of feathers, and entirely helpless. Its first response on hatching is to gape for food, for it has no food reserves.

A male yellow robin presents a beakful of grubs to his mate as she sits on the eggs. This form of cooperation enables the incubating parent to provide continuous warmth for the eggs without suffering a loss of weight or strength.

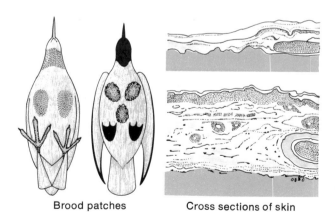

Brood patches   Cross sections of skin

Almost all species of birds develop brood patches, areas on the breast from which the feathers drop off. Patterns differ from one species to another: the phalarope (left) has two, the black-headed gull (right) has three. Richly supplied with blood vessels, the patches transmit warmth to the eggs. Cross sections of skin show the change from the non-breeding condition (above) to the incubation stage (below). The brood patch is thick and engorged with blood.

Among birds such as ducks and geese, the yolk constitutes slightly over a third of the egg. Having this larger supply of food before hatching, a duckling or gosling is down-covered, wide-eyed, and able to follow its mother within a few hours. There are some birds, such as gulls and terns, whose chicks fall between these two extremes—being neither entirely helpless nor entirely mobile at an early age.

The "Sit-In"

For the development of the embryo to proceed normally, the eggs must be kept warm. Boobies and gannets hold their eggs against their bodies by wrapping their webbed feet around their eggs. More often, the eggs are incubated by the parent sitting over them, on a nest.

Most eggs can tolerate a brief chill, when a parent flies off to feed or drink. If the nest is in a cavity, the nest itself retains heat for a time. But if an emperor penguin were to leave his egg even for a minute, the embryo would die, for there is no nest and the below-zero temperatures of Antarctica would cause immediate freezing.

At the other extreme, a Galápagos frigate bird may stand for hours to shade her eggs from the fierce heat of the sun. In the tropics of northern Australia, magpied geese incubate eggs in hot, humid swamps beside flooded plains. In this climate, little heat from the parents is needed.

The bird that has just laid an egg sometimes begins parental chores at once. Herons, hawks, and owls incubate as soon as the first egg is laid, and add other eggs to the clutch while sitting on the nest. Most other species defer incubation until the entire clutch is laid. Ducks, geese, chickens, and many songbirds wait till the last, or next to last, egg has been laid before beginning.

The difference in incubation systems has interesting results. The immediate incubators rear young of different ages. The first to hatch have a head start in their development, for parent birds always feed the largest, most insistent youngsters first. In lean times, the older offspring get everything, and the younger, weaker nestlings starve. Thus the parents may rear fewer offspring, but the survivors will be strong.

When the female does not incubate until the clutch is complete, the eggs laid first develop slowly. They are warmed for a short time whenever the female comes to lay another egg. But full-scale development of embryos does not start until the parent sits continuously.

The chicks of these species generally hatch

The Many Patterns of Incubation

Incubation is an inescapable task. The embryo cannot develop without continuous heat. But the division of labor is often unequal. Many species whose young are well developed at hatching—ducks, grouse, quail— are cared for only by their mothers. For songbirds and seabirds, teamwork is the rule. The greatest variability is in the degree to which the male is involved; some unusual fellows take on the whole job.

When the female incubates alone, she may be entirely solitary, which is the case among mallard ducks. Or like the cardinal, the incubating female may be fed by the male; the female's drab green plumage makes her inconspicuous on the nest. A barn owl female is also assisted by the male while she sits.

Pairs that share incubation chores have different systems. A pileated woodpecker male takes over only at night. Like most seabirds, gannets alternate on the nest. The red-legged partridge has an unusual pattern: The female lays two clutches of eggs in rapid succession, and each parent tends one set.

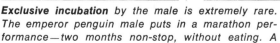

Exclusive incubation by the male is extremely rare. The emperor penguin male puts in a marathon performance—two months non-stop, without eating. A rhea male incubates the eggs of several females. A male phalarope not only incubates alone, but also has the drabber plumage usually characteristic of females.

A European flamingo *rotates its egg by hooking its bill beneath it. This action keeps the eggs evenly warmed and prevents the embryo from sticking to the shell. Almost all birds turn eggs; unturned ones usually do not hatch.*

The Arctic skua announces *its readiness to take over incubation duties by performing a nest-relief ceremony. The bird arches its wings and stretches its neck. The sitting bird will not leave the nest without these formalities.*

within twenty-four hours of one another. The female duck leads all her ducklings to the water at the same time. Sometimes a chick is left behind, still in the shell. Though a few chicks may be lost this way, delayed incubation ensures that the majority of chicks will leave as soon as possible from the nest, where all are more vulnerable to predators.

Incubation is a quiet, peaceful period in a bird's life. To an observer it seems tedious, but the drive to sit is strong. One of a pair may return to the nest with food in its beak, which prompts the sitting bird to leave the nest. In some cases, the returning parent may crowd the other off.

Changing places is often accompanied by a "nest relief" ceremony. The brown pelican approaches its mate in a stately walk, waving its raised head from side to side. The sitting bird lowers its long beak into the nest, giving a low call. Then both birds begin to preen, and one steps from the nest and is replaced.

Incubation duties may be extremely taxing. After the female emperor penguin has laid her single egg, the male jockeys it onto his feet without letting it touch the snow. He tucks the egg under his incubation pouch, covering it completely. The female then leaves the male and waddles off to feed in the sea. In a spectacular display of endurance, the male remains in one place, without eating, for two months. Winds may reach gale force, and the temperatures may drop well below zero, still he is faithful to his task.

The female emperor returns with a crop full of food for the chick just before the egg hatches. If she fails to return on time, the male may be able to regurgitate one meal for the youngster—which is incredible, considering how long it has been since he has eaten. But, of course, if she does not return soon after, the chick dies. When the female arrives, the thin, weary male makes a trek to the sea to feed, and to bring back a crop full of food. Thereafter, they take turns feeding their chick.

The ostrich male also incubates—usually the eggs of several females. In most species, when only one parent incubates, it is the female. She may be entirely alone, as is the pheasant hen, or she may be fed by her mate.

Male and female geese share incubation chores about equally, taking turns on the nest. Among pigeons, doves, and black swans, the females incubate till midmorning. When their mates relieve them, they go off to feed. Late in the afternoon, the females return and again incubate continuously till midmorning.

A mammal embryo is protected within its mother's body. For some, however, there is an interval of great danger

In mammals, there is never a question about who incubates: the mother does it all. From the time of conception, the embryo develops within her body to the point where it is ready for life in the outside world. In the evolution of life on this planet, the rise of mammals represents a giant step forward. The mammalian system of internal "incubation" affords the young total protection over a long period, in a way that does not impede the parent's freedom of movement.

There are two groups of mammals that do not complete their development within the mother's body. One group consists of two egg-laying mammals—the duckbill platypus and the spiny anteater. The other, more numerous, group is composed of the pouched mammals—kangaroo, wallaby, koala, bandicoot, and opossum. Most of these animals live on the island continent of Australia, where they were isolated from the mainstream of evolution. What distinguishes these primitive types from other mammals is that though they nourish their young on milk—which all mammals do—they do not incubate their young the same way.

The duckbill platypus and spiny anteater lay eggs with firm shells. The platypus incubates her eggs in a warm, moist burrow in a riverbank. She curls herself around them, or holds them on her abdomen. The spiny anteater has an incubation pouch in which the eggs are held. When the young spiny anteater hatches, it stays in the pouch till its spines grow. Both species suck milk from the mother's abdominal fur. The milk seeps directly into the fur; these mammals do not have teats.

In pouched mammals, the embryo develops in its mother's uterus for a short time. Generally, once the yolk of the egg is used up, there is no further food available.

In a short time, the embryo must move on if it is to develop further. The embryo, which looks like a tiny red grub at birth, makes its way unaided from the uterus, along the fur of the mother's abdomen, and into her pouch. There the little creature finds a teat. The teat swells in the embryo's mouth, effectively anchoring it to the food supply. Fed by the milk, the embryo continues to develop until it is large, covered with fur, and ready to leave the pouch on its own.

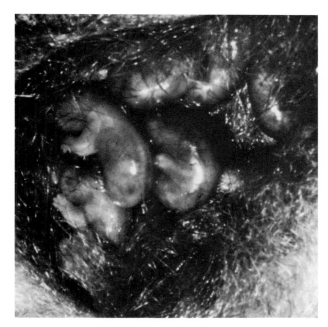

Two weeks after conception, opossum young scramble unaided from their mother's womb to her pouch. The tiny grub-like creatures each find a teat and remain anchored for about sixty-five days. Then, fully furred, they climb out.

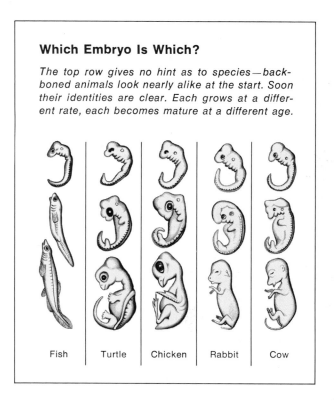

Which Embryo Is Which?

The top row gives no hint as to species—backboned animals look nearly alike at the start. Soon their identities are clear. Each grows at a different rate, each becomes mature at a different age.

Fish   Turtle   Chicken   Rabbit   Cow

A zebra female carries her offspring for about a year. Though the fetus is extremely large relative to its mother's size, the female can keep up with the herd. Minutes after birth, the well-developed youngster trots along beside her.

Lifeline for Embryos

Most mammal embryos are never exposed to such a hazard. The embryos of mice, deer, bears, cats, and myriad other species develop entirely within their mother's body in an uninterrupted process. In these more advanced mammals, the embryo is continuously provided with nutrients from the mother from fertilization to birth.

When the fertilization of the egg occurs—in the upper part of the female's oviduct—the egg makes its way down to the uterus. When it reaches the uterus, it implants there, in the spongy tissue of the wall. A mass of tissue—the placenta—arises from this wall, surrounding the egg and providing a connection between the mother and the developing embryo. The placenta is a two-way filter. It takes oxygen and nutrients from the mother's blood, and returns carbon dioxide and the waste products of the embryo's growth. The blood of

the mother and of the embryo never mix directly.

The placenta is the structure that has allowed for the high degree of development of mammalian young. The mammal mother feeds her embryo from her own body in a gradual process that may continue for months or perhaps more than a year —for African elephants it's twenty-two months.

Some mammals—commonly bears, badgers, weasels, and seals—have a waiting period between the time the egg is fertilized and the time it is implanted in the wall of the uterus. The egg undergoes its first few divisions, and then slows down; it seems to stop growing.

The dormant embryo is retained in the reproductive tract, but does not implant in the uterus wall for several months. The polar bear may carry a fertilized egg for eight or more months before this "delayed implantation" occurs. Then a placenta forms, and the full-scale development

A newborn elephant seal, *its damp coat dusted with sand, wriggles beside its mother. The squawking gulls that land to feed on the afterbirth, and the din of other seals, momentarily distract the pup from nursing. Its mother fasts for three weeks; she loses considerable weight as her nursing pup makes rapid gains—more than tripling its birth weight. Then the female feeds in the sea for a brief time. It is only after she returns (below) that mating takes place. The birth of one pup and the conception of the next occur within a month.*

of the young can begin. In harbor seals, the delay in implantation may be two or three months.

The utility of delayed implantation can be seen in the life cycle of the elephant seal. When these animals come ashore at their traditional breeding grounds, the males collect harems of arriving females. In a short time, the females give birth to their pups, the young of last year's mating, which they nurse for about three weeks. Before leaving the breeding grounds, the females mate and the eggs are fertilized.

Implantation is delayed for four months. After it occurs, the young seals grow rapidly and are ready to be born a short time after their mothers arrive at the breeding grounds the following year. Since both birth and mating must take place on land, the delayed-implantation system allows the females to accomplish both in one trip ashore, rather than two.

The growth of the mammal embryo within its mother's body does not affect her behavior until just before the animal is born. Approaching birth sends the large mammals such as deer off to a secluded part of the woodland. Deer mice, prairie dogs, voles, and other small burrowing mammals often have a nesting area that is the adult's year-round residence.

Other mammals such as wolves find a nest site only to give birth. Whether it be a hollow tree, a burrow dug in the soft, moist earth, or a den abandoned by another animal, the mother may have a few housekeeping chores to make her nest ready. She removes old grass and installs fresh sprigs. Some animals, like the female rabbit, pluck fur from their own bodies to line the nest.

Now the moment has arrived when the young—mammals and birds—come forth and a new cycle of life begins.

Growing Up
in a Family

Many newborn animals are oblivious of everything but the presence of a parent. Like human infants, they cry for attention, and the parents give it zealously

An animal born into a family does not immediately enter the real world; it finds itself instead in a temporary sanctuary created by its parent. Most infants are well hidden or defended from predators, and many do not have to seek food or shelter. Parental care gives them a chance to prepare for independent life.

Nevertheless, birth is often a rough, demanding experience—a time of testing. To survive, an infant animal must assert itself from its earliest moments. A newborn mammal often must struggle for food in competition with littermates. Birds cross the threshold from the passive life within the shell entirely by their own efforts.

Repeatedly jabbing its beak against the shell, a young American robin begins to hatch. The first puncture, near the larger end, is starlike, rimmed with cracks. The bird's body turns slightly with each thrust, and the next chip appears just beside the last. Soon a circle of punctures is formed and the shell splits open. In a series of spasmodic kicks, the hatchling pushes the shell apart and topples out. Exhausted by its efforts, it rests.

A female Canada goose makes a canopy of her body and wings, sheltering her hatching brood. Two goslings, their down already dry and fluffy, stay inside their dark "cave," amid the commotion of lurching eggs. Two days after hatching, the parents escort their young to feeding grounds.

The hatchling's escape from its shell is an extraordinary feat. It has little room to maneuver inside the shell, and just two special tools for the task: a hard, sharp tip on the upper beak called an egg tooth and bands of neck muscles that drive the head forward in short lunges. Soon after the chick is free, the egg tooth drops off and these neck muscles disappear.

Blind and naked, the helpless robin nestling stretches its scrawny neck upward and opens its brilliantly colored mouth, gaping and calling urgently for food. It is soon joined in its appeals by two or three nestmates. The parent birds stuff worms and insects down their mouths, always feeding the loudest, most insistent nestling first.

From dawn to dusk, hard-working robin parents take turns foraging for their hungry brood. At nightfall, the nestlings crouch down to sleep, and their mother settles herself over them, protecting them from the chill of evening.

Most songbird nestlings look almost reptilian, grotesquely unlike their sleek and well-feathered parents. They hatch helpless and naked, capable of little besides begging for food. In contrast, the precocious chicks of quails, ducks, and chickens hatch bright-eyed, covered with downy feathers, and are capable of walking away from the nest within a day or two.

Compared with a chick, a newly hatched nestling seems sluggish, almost pathetic. But what the nestling may lack in alertness and coordination it

A young laughing gull hammers away at its shell with its egg tooth, a limy knob on the upper beak. Depending on species, hatching takes from a few hours to several days.

The porous walls of the shell admit oxygen, but the young bird cannot breathe freely until it has broken an airhole. Thus the early stages of hatching are often the hardest.

Shell Construction

Like the stones in a man-made arch, the crystals of an eggshell are slightly wedge-shaped. The shell can support downward pressure, but breaks when pushed from below. Thus the shell can bear the rubbing of an incubating bird, yet yields to the relatively feeble efforts of a hatchling.

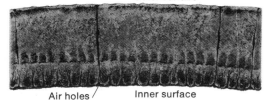

Outer surface

Air holes / Inner surface

A young bird loses its built-in chisel soon after hatching.

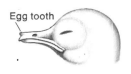

Egg tooth

more than makes up in its capacity for rapid development. It eats its own weight in food each day and grows at a prodigious rate. Three weeks after hatching, a nestling cuckoo has increased its original weight fifty times. The nestling oilbird of northern South America and Trinidad is fed on the oily fruit of the palm. It becomes almost twice as heavy as its parent, and doesn't slim down until its adult plumage begins to appear.

Eggs and nestlings require constant temperatures. Before their feathers form, nestlings are unable to keep warm by themselves. In many species, one parent broods—sitting with its body or wings covering the young—while the other forages. Overexposure to sun may be as hazardous as chilling, and some parents respond by shading the nest. The instinctive nature of this urge was demonstrated by an experiment in which the nestlings of a red-backed shrike were removed: the female continued to shade the empty nest. The nestlings, which were temporarily placed on the ground, cried in vain for her attention!

Like most songbirds, *nestling great tits hatch out blind, naked, and utterly dependent on their parents. All they can do on their own behalf is gape and call for food.*

In contrast to songbird nestlings, *Hudsonian curlew chicks are down-covered and wide-eyed at hatching. They live on body reserves for a day or so, then forage for themselves.*

Well-Developed Chicks

A few days before hatching, sounds begin coming from a clutch of quail's eggs. Unlike songbird nestlings, chicks cheep while still in the shell. After the first soft sounds, the quail hen may go off briefly to feed, but thereafter she remains on the nest continuously, neither feeding nor drinking until she leads the young away.

The quail hen had secretively visited her nest daily for fifteen days, laying an egg each time. On the last day she remained on the nest. Because the embryos do not begin full-scale growth until they are warmed continuously, all the chicks began breaking out of their shells on the same day. The cheeping in the shells may have helped to synchronize hatching.

Though newly hatched quails are far more developed than nestling songbirds, they cannot survive without their mother. Her body keeps the air in the nest warm and humid. But for her presence, a hatching chick would dry too quickly and its down would stick to the shell membranes, trapping it. These membranes, and the cord that attached the chick to the yolk sac, have a tendency to become tough when dried. Then, too, without its mother to warm it, the chick would be chilled and weakened by the rapid evaporation of moisture as its feathers dried off.

In a short time, their mottled brown and yellow down becomes dry and fluffy, and the chicks come out from under their mother's feathers. The hen leads her brood from the shell-strewn nest out into the field. The irregular shapes and light insides of broken shells attract predators, but for birds such as quails and ducks that leave the nest quickly, the hazard is brief.

Many parent birds remove foreign matter from the nest—twigs, leaves, or dead young. Once the hatchlings have kicked themselves free, the shells, too, are removed. The parents keep flying off with the cracked shells in their beaks until the nest is cleared; simply dumping them out would advertise the presence of the nest. Thus crowding is relieved and the nest is kept inconspicuous.

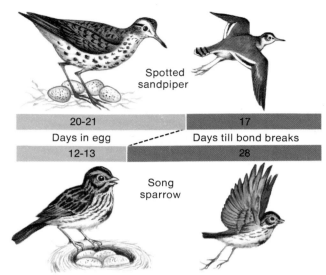

20-21	17
Days in egg	Days till bond breaks
12-13	28

Spotted sandpiper

Song sparrow

Comparing two species *that achieve independence at about the same age—thirty-eight to forty days—there is a great difference in how the time is spent. A precocious spotted sandpiper, which can walk soon after hatching, spends more time in the egg than a song sparrow. A sparrow hatches at about twelve days, but is then helpless.*

Too much heat *may be as harmful as too little. A pair of five-day-old laughing gull chicks take refuge from the sun in their parent's shadow. When the adult moves, the young skitter along, reestablishing themselves in the shade. As they grow older, their own plumage protects them.*

Young sandwich terns and kittiwakes have highly visible markings, and for these and other conspicuous species, the presence of a few shells makes little difference. The parents are not so meticulous; fragments are frequently left in the general litter of the nest. The security of the young depends primarily on the constant attendance of one or both parents.

A brood of nestlings is generally smaller than a brood of chicks. A robin pair is hard-pressed to find enough food to satisfy four demanding nestlings. A partridge hen, on the other hand, merely leads her twelve to eighteen chicks to an appropriate place, and they forage for themselves. The only limit to the size of a partridge's brood seems to be the number of eggs she is able to cover with her body.

Quail chicks—and ducklings, goslings, and many other young birds—have a food reserve at the time of hatching that sustains them for a while. They do not feed during the two days or less that they are in the nest. It is at this time that the importance of simultaneous hatching becomes clear. Since the chicks must go where the food is, they must leave the nest before their body resources are exhausted. If the first-hatched chicks had to wait three or four days while the other eggs hatched, they would starve to death.

The trek to the feeding grounds is often arduous. Eider ducks hatch their broods on small islands off the coast of Britain. On bleak, gray mornings in late spring, tiny convoys of ducks appear bobbing on the waves of the North Sea. The ducklings follow their mother from the soft, downy world of the nest, across the rocky shore, and into the water. Two miles of open sea is a formidable obstacle for the youngsters, but they trail their mother in close formation as she swims toward the shores of Northumberland. There, shepherded by their mother, the young ducks feed in the bountiful marshes.

A brood of muscovy ducklings plods determinedly after their mother, replying to her constant calling with tiny piping voices. By the time they leave the nest, they are firmly imprinted on her, and will follow no other creature.

Imprinting — The Immediate Bond

To follow their mother, precocial ducklings and chicks must be able to recognize her. The recognition process begins even before they hatch, when they first hear their mother's voice. During the first day or so of their lives, the chicks follow anything that moves — generally the enormous pair of legs and towering "cloud formation" of feathers that is their mother. Her familiar call helps to keep them close.

In the wild, the chances of the young birds' even seeing another adult are slight, for the mother drives off all other creatures. The chicks gradually learn to recognize her by sight. By the end of the second day most precocial chicks avoid anything that moves except their mother. This remarkably quick attachment is called imprinting.

Occasionally, mistakes do occur, and young birds become imprinted on the wrong adult bird. At first such a mistake has no serious consequences, for the foster mothers rear the "ugly ducklings" as they do their own. Only when the young reach maturity does it make a difference to the adopted birds. They will attempt to court and mate with birds of their foster mothers' species.

Konrad Lorenz, an Austrian scientist well known for his studies of animal behavior, has carried out many imprinting experiments on greylag geese. The hand-reared broods of geese at his laboratory

Exodus from the Nest

In the darkness of the nest cavity, newly hatched wood ducks develop a bond with their mother based entirely on the sound of her voice. At two days, she calls to them from the water. They teeter at the nest, then drop down near her to feed.

A quintet of yellow-tailed thornbills appeals to a parent for food. For the adult, the sight of the brightly colored mouths is an irresistible stimulus; it will stuff any gaping young that it finds in its own nest, even a stranger.

Stealing Parental Care

Indian wren warbler

Great reed warbler

Brown babbler

Plaintive cuckoo

Common cuckoo

Jacobin cuckoo

Parasitic birds escape parental duties by leaving their eggs in another birds' nests. An Indian warbler, for example, may rear a young, plaintive cuckoo. Look-alike eggs aid in the deception.

Cuckoo

Honeyguide

A newly hatched European cuckoo disposes of its rivals by dumping the eggs out of the nest. The honeyguide kills nestmates with its sharp beak.

in Bavaria become imprinted on their human caretakers. Lorenz found that the greylag goslings—which show no fear—imprinted more quickly when he crouched down and honked as he led them. When mature, these geese courted him as he swam in the lake beside the laboratory.

To establish an attachment with timorous mallard ducklings, Lorenz had to simulate mallard sounds. In other laboratory studies, it was discovered that young mallards have an instinctive preference for the maternal calls of their own species. With several mechanical models emitting various maternal calls, these ducklings invariably chose the right species though they had not heard the sounds of adult mallards before, even while they were still in the egg.

Small caged birds such as the zebra finch also become imprinted on humans when they are reared by hand from the nestling stage. When adult, the male will court its owner's finger, or fly onto his shoulder and court his ear. The bird's attachment is to the human, but he chooses as the object of his attentions only parts of the human body that are about his own size.

Brood Parasites

High-quality parental care, given instinctively to the occupants of the family nest, provides an opportunity for the parasitic way of life adopted by European cuckoos and American cowbirds. Avoiding the burdens of parenthood, the female cuckoo is able to concentrate her energies on the production of eggs for others to rear.

The European cuckoo female keeps several nests under surveillance. When the female of a suitable host species, perhaps a redstart, lays an egg and leaves the nest, the cuckoo lays one of her own with remarkable speed—in a matter of seconds. Then the cuckoo either flies off with her host's egg in her bill or leaves it for the cuckoo nestling to deal with after hatching.

The redstart is inclined to accept the egg as one of her own. Other birds may eject it, or as sometimes happens when the host is a wood warbler, the parent may abandon the nest, build a new one, and lay a second clutch of eggs.

The young European cuckoo hatches before the other eggs in its foster parents' nest. For the first days of its life, the young parasite will labor to

Although dwarfed by its foster nestling, *a gray fantail continues to feed the young cuckoo. Birds respond not to their own young, but to the widest gape, the most urgent call. Meanwhile, the nest's rightful occupant cries in vain for food.*

throw out of the nest all other eggs and chicks. Though blind and featherless, it has strong muscles. When a sensitive spot on its back touches a solid object, the nestling shoves it upward, sometimes somersaulting in an effort to flip it out of the nest. Once the nest is cleared of rivals, the young cuckoo has the undivided attention of its foster parents.

The African honeyguide, another parasitic bird, has a different system; the nestling honeyguide kills its nestmates—the young of its hosts—with needle-sharp hooks on its beak. The parents remove the dead nestlings and the honeyguide has the nest to itself. At about two weeks, the honeyguide loses its lethal spikes.

When parasites become plentiful, there is a risk that they will destroy their hosts, and ultimately themselves. But usually, wherever there is parasitism, there is a balance between the numbers of parasites and their hosts. Indeed, most parasites do a minimum of harm to their hosts.

The parasitic American cowbird, for example, lives peacefully with its foster siblings. Widow birds lay their eggs in the nests of their close relatives, the weaver finches. The widow birds are extremely specialized parasites whose eggs and young closely resemble those of their hosts, even to the details of gapes and calls. The nestlings of host and parasite grow together in harmony, fledge together, then separate. The parasite has been reared, but so also have all but one of the host's brood.

Generally, the cost of parasitism is well within the host's ability to pay. Other parasitic birds ensure against the destruction of their hosts by holding large territories—that is, excluding other parasites—or by parasitizing a wide range of hosts.

The young parasite grows to maturity having little or no contact with its own species. Yet when mature, cuckoos mate with cuckoos, and never with the adults of their foster species. Parasitic birds neither imprint on their foster parents nor learn from them. The parasites have instead an instinctive response to adults of their own species. The only kind of learning that takes place seems to be in the choice of host. In populations of European cuckoos, members of each "tribe" tend to parasitize the same host species.

For some mammals, birth is a rude awakening — a jolt as the infant drops, a cold-water bath, or a flight from predators

The birth of a mammal is a smoothly ordered sequence of events in which the young animal makes the transition from the passive life in the womb to an active engagement with entirely new surroundings. The mother is not only a partner in the birth but is also, in a real sense, the essence of the newborn's environment. A mammal is always born into a world of its mother's making, in which she is the youngster's most important experience.

Danger surrounds the moment of birth, for even the most powerful of mothers is relatively helpless while delivering her young. Flight is impossible and even defense is limited. The young, which were effectively protected while they developed in their mothers' bodies, share the hazard. Most mammals are small burrowers, which find security underground, or in holes in trees. Larger mammals seek out a secluded spot to give birth — some move only to the edge of the herd.

Certain antelopes, giraffes, elephants, and a number of other large mammals give birth while standing; the first experience of their young is a jolt as they land on the ground. Usually, a young giraffe's front feet appear first, followed by the head. The calf blinks its eyes and begins breathing as soon as its head emerges. Less than ten minutes later, it topples to the ground from the considerable height of its mother's body.

The mother black bear gives birth in her den during the period of her winter sleep. The cubs — usually two or three — weigh only about a half pound at birth. Nursed and warmed in the den during the long winter, they emerge in spring the size of spaniels, fully furred and ready to explore.

Most mammals lie down to give birth, especially the smaller nesting creatures. Laboratory rats have been seen helping the process along by pulling on the emerging young with mouth and paws. Because burrowers are secretive at the time of birth, it is not known how common this may be.

If the umbilical cord is not broken during the birth process, it is bitten through by the mother shortly after the delivery. Once the infant inhales its first breath of air, the cord connecting it to the oxygen of its mother's blood is unnecessary. The newborn's crucial first gulp of air may be blocked by birth membranes that cover the nose and mouth. Suffocation is rare because usually the mother licks the nose and head of the infant.

The mammal mother usually sets to work with vigor to lick her infant's coat dry. The young are born wet, and the evaporation of moisture is likely to chill them. Birth fluids that saturate the newborn's coat are attractive to the mother, and this "candy coating" on infants ensures immediate attention. Most mothers go on to eat the placenta, which is also saturated with fluids — even though they may otherwise be exclusively vegetarian. The placental tissues may contain hormones that stimulate the flow of milk. Then too, they are fragile and decompose rapidly. By eating them, the mother removes a source of smells that could attract a predator.

The rough pummeling of the mother's tongue stimulates the circulation of the infant's blood, and clears its digestive tract by stimulating the first bowel movement. Young sheep and goats may die or fail to do well if they do not get this maternal care during the first few hours of life.

The warm-blooded, air-breathing whales give birth near the surface of the sea. The young come forth tail first, and their mothers often prod them to the surface for their first breath. The sperm whale calf is about fourteen feet long at birth and usually weighs about a ton. Its one-inch coat of blubber is not thick enough to prevent its feeling the shock of the cold water. As an adult, this layer of insulation will be about a foot thick.

Propped at the surface of the sea, the youngster gains strength as it breathes. The wallowing of the two great creatures soon tears away the navel cord, and seabirds dive down to feed on the floating mass of the placenta.

In a short time, the sperm whale calf begins to seek the teats, awkwardly pummeling its mother's body in its search. Finally it finds them in a slit in her abdomen. She extrudes a teat and, lying on her side near the surface, squirts the rich, nourishing milk into the calf's mouth.

Seals and walruses are nearly as much at home in the sea as whales, but they do not give birth

A newborn zebra wriggles free of its birth sac. Within ten minutes of birth, it tries out its wobbly legs. The foal begins searching for a teat as soon as its mother stands. At a half hour, the youngster can trot along with the herd.

The porpoise, *like larger whales, is born tail-first. When it has fully emerged, its mother gently nudges it to the surface for its first breath of air; otherwise it might drown. Other females often rally round to help support it.*

there. Their young first see the light of day on a rocky shore or perhaps an ice floe.

A female Alaska fur seal hauls up on the beach at the Tolstoi rookery of St. Paul Island, off Alaska, and gives birth amid the cries of multitudes of other seals. Her pup receives no help from her, either in delivery or in freeing itself of birth membranes. She nuzzles its body, breathing in its scent: by its smell she will later identify it in the crowds of youngsters that sprawl and bleat throughout the colony. But now, with the umbilical cord and placenta dragging, the newborn seal searches for a teat. Nursing seems to be the only care given by this inattentive mother.

The sum total of the mother's and infant's behavior at birth—licking, sniffing, nursing, calling, whatever it may be—focuses the attention of mother and infant on each other. This is the first step in bond-formation. Any omission or interference impairs the relationship—and the young animal's chances for survival.

Nomadic mammals, and especially herd animals, must build bonds quickly. Mother and offspring must be able to find one another in the crowd. The bond between a lamb and its ewe or a calf and its dam develops as swiftly and surely as the imprinting of a duckling on its mother.

A rhesus monkey gives birth while the troop pauses to feed or rest. At first a powerful one-sided bond develops, as the mother becomes attached to her youngster. Later, when the infant is older, the bond becomes reciprocal.

The monkey mother gives birth surrounded by adults, which groom her fur. They generally attempt to touch the newborn shortly after birth. The mother permits them to inspect her infant, but usually holds it firmly while they do so.

Young mammals born in nests bond with their mothers eventually, just as nestling birds become attached to their parents. The bond is not established at once, but by the time a young raccoon is old enough to venture from the nest, parent and offspring can easily identify one another.

The First-Time Mother

Little is known about the early stages of maternal behavior of small burrowing mammals because the nests are inaccessible. Studies of laboratory rats show that the first litter is born and cared for without incident, and the inexperienced mother does as well as the experienced one.

But large mammals are not automatically successful mothers. Young females often seem confused; they may even be afraid of their first offspring. The youngsters themselves are likely to be somewhat undersized or weak. Frequently an elephant cow's first calf is stillborn. Even when reared, the firstborn may not be as robust as later offspring. One explanation is that the first birth is a trial run that prepares the mother's body for future births.

At the Basle zoo in Switzerland, a young giraffe gave birth to her first calf. Apparently distressed, she sniffed the calf briefly, then walked away to feed. When she returned she circled it, clumsily stepping on one of its legs. After the calf toppled over repeatedly during its attempts to stand, the keepers entered the pen and discovered that the leg was broken. In the wild, such an infant would have died. In this case, a veterinarian set the leg.

When the calf was returned to its mother, she took no interest in it whatsoever. The moment of bonding had passed. Having failed to lick and sniff it sufficiently to learn its scent, she had no way of knowing that it belonged to her. The calf was removed to the zoo nursery and fed cow's milk.

Young monkey mothers, too, tend to be less skillful than older, more experienced females. A first-time mother can be quite unnerved by the whining and struggling of her infant. She may handle it awkwardly, even though she has often played with infants before becoming a mother.

An infant langur prefers close body contact and becomes restless and complaining if held too loosely. Experienced mothers are more relaxed, but firm nonetheless; frequently they will come to the aid of a squirming youngster in the arms of an inexperienced mother.

A giraffe may be six feet tall at birth and weigh about 100 pounds. Birth takes place slightly apart from the herd, and is generally swift. As befits a plains animal with no defenses against predators except flight, a young giraffe is soon able to stand and follow its mother back to the herd. Within two days, it can keep up when the adults run. Though birth in the wild has been studied in many species, the closest observations have been made in zoos, where it is easier and the stakes are high—for zoo specimens are expensive. There is a growing realization that for some animals, zoos will be the last refuge, since their habitats throughout the world are being destroyed. In one zoo study, a first-time mother giraffe walked around her calf counterclockwise, the reverse of the direction normally taken. This alerted the keepers to the fact that things were not going well. On such hard-won bits of information rests the future of many creatures that must ultimately be bred and reared in zoos, or perish from the Earth.

The appetites of nestlings are often so voracious that both parents must work full time to satisfy them

Nestlings grow rapidly if their parents provide food at the proper rate. The food-collecting efforts of the parents must be matched to the appetites of the young.

That the calls of nestlings control the food-gathering of the parents was shown in an experiment with pied flycatchers. A brood of seven nestlings was separated: six were placed in a closed nest box, the other in an open box. The parents could hear the six, but they could feed only the single, exposed nestling. Spurred on by the plaintive cries of the six, they stuffed the youngster with more than twice its normal rations. The urgent feeding calls of the adults drove the hidden six almost frantic. When the six were released, the pair continued feeding until all were satisfied, and the young ceased calling. Clearly the parents made no assessment of the food requirements, but merely responded to the behavior of their young.

The equal sharing of food is also ensured by the behavior of the young. The hungrier the nestling, the more it calls, and the more vigorously it gapes. On the other hand, the nestling that has just been fed cannot swallow again at once, and the food sits in its mouth. The adult retrieves such morsels and crams them into another mouth. Eventually all will be fed to satiation, though the strongest and hungriest are fed first. Only when the young are completely satisfied do the parents take a few minutes off to feed themselves.

Normally, nothing short of extreme hunger and distress will induce nestlings to call and gape when the parents are away from the nest. Here the survival value is in not attracting a predator. When the adult returns, gaping is triggered by the rush of the parent's wings, the vibration it makes as it lands on the nest, or perhaps the shadow it casts. If the nestlings do not gape immediately, the parent gives a feeding call and arouses the sleepy young.

The appetites of young birds increase precipitously as they grow. When European nuthatch nestlings are two days old, they are fed about 120 times daily; when they are twenty days old, and almost ready to fledge, they are fed approximately 335 times daily!

Before the demands of the nestlings exceed the ability of one parent to forage, their feathers grow out. The young birds can then keep themselves warm for longer periods because they are developing not only an insulating body covering but body heat as well. This releases a parent from brooding duty; both are free to serve the increasing appetites.

Division of labor between parents is not necessarily equal. The Arctic warbler male makes only 25 per cent of the trips for food, but he tends to bring more in his beak each time than the female. Parents often change roles as their young grow. When her nestlings are about to fledge, the female house wren deserts them, builds a new nest, and begins laying her second clutch of eggs. The male takes over the feeding of the young.

Songbirds commonly make about forty feeding trips an hour (the great tit has been reported to make as many as sixty, or about 900 a day). But pelicans bring food only one to three times a day, and albatrosses just two to five times a week.

The frequency of feeding depends on many things—the type of food, the method of foraging, the age of the young, and the distance the parent must fly to collect or capture food. When a songbird catches a few insects in its territory, it immediately carries the food back in its beak to the nest. Because distances are short and the insects light, the bird makes many trips. By contrast, one of the larger hunting birds may glide or hover for hours before it captures suitable prey—a snake, lizard, frog, mouse, or other bird. And then the hawk, eagle, or osprey may have to carry the heavy carcass many miles back to the nest.

Protein for Growth

The hunters make fewer and longer trips than songbirds, but each kill is rich in protein, often enough to stay the appetites of nestlings for several days. Many other birds also hunt miles from their nest, especially those that gather food in the ocean. The white pelicans nesting on islands in Great Salt Lake may fly as much as 100 miles in search of food—for the lake is too briny to support sufficient food for them.

Growing animals need protein. Because game, fish, and insects are rich in this body-building substance, flesh-eating birds do not have to make any adjustments in their food-hunting habits to feed their nestlings. But because seeds, nectar, and fruits are low in protein, vegetarian birds must collect both types of food: insects for their nestlings and plant foods for themselves. A cardinal

Eager for a meal, *a white pelican chick nearly disappears down its parent's throat pouch in search of fish. When first hatched, the chicks are fed regurgitated food in liquid form, which the parents dribble into their bills.*

The first food *of mourning dove nestlings is crop-milk, a white, semifluid secretion from the parents' crops. In about five days, the parents resume feeding, and when the squabs dive down, they feed on both milk and grain.*

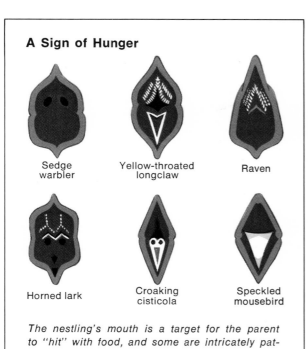

A Sign of Hunger

Sedge
warbler

Yellow-throated
longclaw

Raven

Horned lark

Croaking
cisticola

Speckled
mousebird

The nestling's mouth is a target for the parent to "hit" with food, and some are intricately patterned. Nestlings that hatch in semidarkness may even have iridescent spots that guide a parent.

The red spot on a herring gull's bill *is highly attractive to its offspring. A peck here stimulates the parents to regurgitate semidigested food in front of the chick. As the chicks get older, they wander, and peck any adult's bill.*

Two half-grown cattle egrets jab wildly in their attempt to catch a parent's bill. One succeeds in getting a crosswise grip. As it tugs, food is transferred. In other species, such as the albatross, the parents do the grasping.

was observed pausing on the way to its nest with a bill full of grubs. The bird dropped the grubs, fed itself on sunflower seeds, then picked up the grubs again and delivered them to its nestlings.

Many birds swallow their food whole and carry it to the young in crop, gullet, or pouch. Adult herring gulls regurgitate food into the nest; heron parents regurgitate it into the young birds' mouths. Pelicans allow the young to plunge head first into their throats and feed directly from the food-filled bill pouches.

Adult pigeons and doves feed on grain, a good food for them but a poor one for their rapidly growing squabs. After the young hatch, the parents' crops become swollen with a milky substance called crop-milk. It is a highly nutritious food resembling the milk of mammals. The squabs feed exclusively on crop-milk for about five days, and then on milk-softened seeds for the next eighteen days as the proportion of milk decreases.

One of the most bizarre feeding arrangements is that of the tropical boobies. Generally boobies lay two eggs and the young hatch several days apart. Because the older nestling can compete more effectively for food, the difference in size and strength rapidly increases. In times of acute food shortage, the older nestling kills and eats its smaller sibling, thus ensuring that at least one healthy youngster fledges.

Precocial chicks can wait a day or so after hatching to eat. The mother does not bring food to them; she takes them to the food. The jungle fowl hen, for example, leads her chicks from the nest on their second day of life. She scratches vigorously under bushes, clucking rapidly when she finds a grub; she then drops it for them.

Sometimes the hen squawks loudly and, puffing out her feathers, leads the brood away from a spider or brightly colored wasp. These are not to be eaten. With such a tutor, the chicks quickly learn how to feed themselves, although they depend for a long time on their mother's ability to scratch in the damp soil. By the time they are six weeks old, her powerful scratching is the only help they get; she no longer offers them tidbits. Such precocial chicks eat mainly insects at first. When they are full-grown, they gradually switch from high-protein insects to high-energy plant foods such as seeds and berries.

Some precocial chicks ride piggyback for a time. Mute-swan and grebe chicks nestle on the backs of their swimming parents and wait for food to be passed to them. Later the young swim alongside their parents, begging from each in turn.

A Special Problem in Nest Sanitation

Few birds rear their young in greater security than the hornbills of Africa. After mating, the pair finds a hollow tree. They seal the opening with the female inside, using a plaster of mud, droppings, and regurgitated food. A narrow slit is left, through which the male feeds his mate. Safe from monkeys and tree snakes, the female lays and incubates from one to six eggs. When the young hatch, the entire family is fed by the father. The mother is kept busy distributing food, and throwing out wastes and her own molted feathers. When their mother leaves, the young reseal the nest, and both parents bring food until the youngsters are ready to break out of their own accord.

A hornbill pair occupies an abandoned woodpecker nest. They seal the entrance with the female inside.

The female keeps house by slipping feathers, feces, and other debris out through the feeding slit.

As the nestlings get larger, the female departs, sealing the nest up again. The young help with the job.

Nest Sanitation

A dirty nest could be dangerous. The scent might attract predators, and an accumulation of droppings could harbor enough parasites to kill otherwise protected nestlings. Housekeeping, which begins with the disposal of eggshells, continues as long as the young stay in one place.

A cliff swallow glides gracefully to its cup-shaped mud nest, its beak filled with insects. As the gust of air from its wings sweeps over its nestlings, they call and gape for food. The parent stuffs the insects into the first mouth to engage its attention. Momentarily satisfied, the nestling settles back, only to pop up a moment later, this time tail first. A soft white sac is extruded. The parent seizes it and flies off to drop it away from the nest.

Many young songbirds excrete their feces and concentrated urine in such membranous sacs, thus enabling their parents to carry all waste products away from the nest. The female lyrebird of the Australian forest takes sanitation a step further by depositing the sacs in pools, where they disintegrate in a natural sewage system. Songbird parents of many species eat the fecal sacs. The incompletely digested food of the young is a valuable supplement to their diet at a time when they are devoting nearly all their energies to feeding the nestlings.

The great horned owl is a good provider but a poor housekeeper. Its nest gradually fills up with the bones, heads, feet, and skins of prey. Pigeons, too, are untidy. As the nestlings approach fledging, mites and other vermin accumulate in the untidy nest. They feed on droppings and on the young themselves, causing itching and possibly disease.

Because pigeons generally nest above the ground, their miserable housekeeping results merely in discomfort. But a related species, the ruddy ground dove, which nests in the grass, carefully removes all wastes. Because its nest is readily accessible to predators, good housekeeping is a matter of survival for the ground dove.

*A **beaver mother nurses** a trio of kits in the company of the infants' father. The kits are born with their eyes open and with a soft coat of fur. They begin eating solid food at four weeks, and are completely weaned at six weeks of age.*

Life in a Beaver Lodge

Beavers are unusual because they pair for life and the male participates in the care of their kits. Litters range in size from one to eight. In the spring, when a new litter is born, the young of the previous year remain, but the two-year-olds are evicted. These youngsters travel far from home in search of a mate and a suitable place to build their own establishment.

*The **lodge is built** by a pair of young beavers before the first litter arrives. It is a great conical pile of sticks and mud, plastered together. The entrances are well below the surface of the water—an artificial lake formed by the beavers' dam. Few animals are able to invade the lodge, so the beaver kits are comparatively safe while at home.*

A parent assists a two-week-old kit out of the water with handlike front paws. The infants take readily to the water, but do not leave the lodge by themselves at this age. An adult guides them through the long tunnel to the outside.

Two young beavers cruise beside a parent, watching as the adult collects twigs. The beaver's remarkable skill in construction is influenced by learning. The young serve a long apprenticeship, helping to repair the dam and lodge.

Shoved from behind, a tired, soggy beaver kit returns from a swim in the pond. During these early expeditions, kits hold on to an adult's fur or tail with their teeth. If they detach, the parent rounds them up with its paws or teeth.

When a young mammal tries to nurse, it often finds that it is on a strict schedule

One by one, the wild sow delivers her piglets and they slide into the rough, grassy nest she has prepared. Within a minute the firstborn piglet scrambles to its feet and lurches toward the large dark bulk of the sow. Momentarily restrained by the umbilical cord still attached to its navel, it tugs free and presses its snout against the sow's warm body.

At first her stiff bristles prick its tender skin, but the piglet quickly learns to follow the "down-hair" path of least resistance which leads to the midline of the udder. Using a ring of sensitive whiskers around its snout, it locates a nipple.

In a short time, the firstborn piglet is joined by its littermates. Each seizes a nipple and begins nursing. Soon some piglets are shopping around for better ones. The forward nipples, which have the strongest milk flow, are the most sought after.

Now the piglets begin fighting over teats. They snap so fiercely with their needle-sharp teeth that their faces are thoroughly scratched after a few hours. By the end of the first day most have settled down to their own teats. A piglet that has lost a preferred position may fight for it repeatedly at every feeding. Sometimes a loser may die of starvation, so strong is this teat attachment.

For the first few hours, the piglets nurse at will, often falling asleep with the teats in their mouths.

Later in the day, the sow begins to call them to feed every thirty or forty minutes. Her snorts, slow and rhythmic at first, attract the piglets to the udder, where each takes its teat and tugs.

There is no milk at first, but gradually the tempo of the sow's snorting increases until it is almost continuous. At this point the sow "lets down" her milk, then she stops snorting while her young lean back, sucking furiously on the teats. In about a minute, the flow stops as suddenly as it started. Let down is finished. The piglets continue to tug on the teats, draining the last few drops.

One or two piglets may walk up and touch the sow's snout, indicating that they want to continue feeding. But she does not respond. She has set a pattern of feeding that will continue until she weans her offspring in three months. The litter is always ready to feed before their mother is prepared to feed them, and she must drive them away several times before each meal. The intervals between feedings gradually increase, reaching almost two hours just before weaning.

The value of teat attachment seems to be that the young waste little time scrambling for a place when the mother is ready to nurse. Then too, by regularly nursing at one teat each youngster always gets one that is functioning. How widespread teat attachment may be is not known.

For the single precocial offspring of deer, zebras, buffaloes, and rhinoceroses, there is no competition, and the female has fewer teats—two or perhaps four. Sometimes it is important for the young to find the right angle to approach the teat, which is otherwise out of reach between its mother's

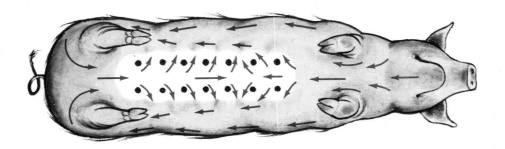

The hair pattern of the sow is like a prickly road map for the piglets. They follow directions to find a teat.

Immediately after birth, piglets compete fiercely for the forward teats, where the milk supply is most abundant. The largest piglets win. The advantage of additional food gets them started toward higher social rank in the litter.

With sweeping strokes, a cougar grooms her spotted, six-week-old youngsters as they nurse. Maternal care is much like that of household cats. For a short time after birth, the mother is available constantly; later she withdraws more and more. By four months her offspring are weaned, but they depend on her hunting skill for up to two years.

On a warm, drowsy afternoon in Nairobi National Park, a vervet mother is groomed by another female while her infant absentmindedly lets the nipple slip. At this age, a youngster is held much of the time and can nurse whenever it wants.

A harbor seal pup is born in the sea, where it floats vertically. Its mother nurses and shepherds the pup till it can haul up on land. Thereafter, it is nursed ashore. This pup has shed its infant coat and will soon be independent.

hind legs. The female mouse deer of Asia raises one hind leg off the ground to give access.

Mammalian young are permitted to drink at will immediately after birth, but gradually a feeding schedule emerges, with regular intervals between meals. The mother sets the timetable, though the young often make their demands known by attempting to suckle before she is ready. A Grant's gazelle signals to her young to feed by waving her head. The sucking of the young completes the sequence that leads to the let-down of her milk, which is usually of short duration.

Feeding schedules vary from one species to another. A young monkey clinging to its mother's fur is never far from her teats, and seems able to nurse whenever it wants. It may often be seen peering out at the world with a nipple in its mouth. At the other extreme, the furry, bright-eyed young of the tree shrew are left alone in the nest, visited by their mother only once every two days for nursing.

The female marmoset monkey of the South American rain forests usually gives birth to twins. The male carries the two infants around, protecting them from all the dangers of their leafy world. He cannot feed them however, and so delivers them one at a time to their mother for nursing.

The appetites of the young monkeys increase as they grow, and at first the mother's milk flow keeps pace with their demands. Then milk production levels off, and the feeding schedule begins to change. They pester their mother, and are regularly rebuffed. As the interval between feedings lengthens, they must look for other food. Thus the weaning process begins. The milk supply diminishes—slowly at first, then more rapidly.

Young grazing mammals switch from milk to adult food with relative ease. Grass is all around them and they soon begin nibbling. Wildebeest calves start grazing within a few days, but they are exceptionally well-developed infants, able to run with the herd on the day they are born. Most young mammals feed exclusively on milk for some weeks or months.

A young ape or monkey starts on solids by taking food from its mother's mouth, or by reaching out for fruit and leaves while she feeds. Because the chimpanzee infant is venturesome in its eating, its mother must constantly snatch inappropriate fruits and greens away from it. Many rodents such as kangaroo rats and pocket gophers hoard dried hay or bury nuts in their nests. In the course of exploring their underground homes, the rodent young discover and eat the food.

Aids to Digestion

Most young plant-eating mammals are not immediately able to adapt to an adult diet. Raw plant tissue is often relatively indigestible because it contains tough fibers—the cellulose that gives bulk and structure to plants. The stomachs or intestines of the adult plant-eaters contain microscopic single-celled organisms that help to digest such coarse foods. Young herbivores are not born with these microorganisms; they must acquire them. A young roe deer starts his adult feeding by eating earth; soil contains a variety of microorganisms.

For an infant koala, the organisms can come only from its mother, who feeds entirely on leaves of eucalypt trees. Preparation for this diet takes about a month, and begins when the young koala eats partly digested eucalypt leaves passed through the mother's digestive tract every second day; these are not her feces. The youngster takes them as it leans from her pouch, and thus introduces

An introduction to the adult food of a species may take place quite casually. A wallaby youngster, lounging in its mother's pouch, sticks its head out and manages to nibble on a leaf from the same bush on which she is feeding.

Care of the fur is essential to the health of mammals, and the inclination to groom is instinctive. A young Tasmanian scrub wallaby licks its mother's ear, while she licks the youngster's feet. The relatively large joey can still crowd into its mother's pouch, a portable nursery that is also subject to constant inspection and cleaning.

the necessary microorganisms into its own digestive system. Young rodents such as hamsters, shrews, and hares acquire these microorganisms by eating their mother's droppings.

Adult food is not as readily available to young flesh-eaters as it is to young plant-eaters. The flesh-eaters must be taught to hunt. Well before lessons begin, the young are introduced to adult food, which supplements the waning milk supply. A lioness may drag a kill to the cubs, or she may gorge herself and then regurgitate for her young when she returns to them.

Food-sharing has reached its highest development among the mammals in the dog family—the wolves, coyotes, and hunting dogs. The parents, or indeed the whole pack, eat their fill after the prey is killed. Then they regurgitate until the appetites of the pups are satisfied.

Mammal Housekeeping

Nest sanitation is a problem for mammals as well as for birds. A young kangaroo or wallaby lives in a portable nest, the pouch in its mother's body. While the young kangaroo or wallaby, called a joey, is still in the pouch, its mother grooms it, stimulating elimination and removing wastes at once, so that the pouch is always clean.

Housekeeping is easier when the young help. Shortly after it is born, a young piglet walks away from the sow to defecate or urinate. As soon as the piglet loses physical contact with the sow, it begins to grunt softly and regularly; immediately the sow answers with similar, deeper grunts. These location calls continue until the youngster is reunited with its mother. Thus the nest is kept clean without any of the piglets becoming lost in the process.

For the precocial young of deer, wild asses, bison, goats, and similar animals, there is no problem of hygiene, for the herd is always on the move. Droppings are not a problem for monkeys and apes either. They usually travel and rest in trees, and their waste products simply fall through the branches to the ground. Thus it is easy to understand why primates cannot be housebroken when humans attempt to keep them as pets; they have no natural behavior of this kind in the wild.

A seal rookery is a squalid place; the mother does not clean up after birth, nor do any of the seals leave the area to discharge wastes. The high infant mortality in a rookery can be largely attributed to the filthy conditions; the young frequently pick up the eggs of parasites from the feces of adults.

The tactics animals use in defense of their offspring range from direct attack to subtle deception

Musk oxen under attack by a pack of wolves form a defensive circle with the calves at the center. The wolves cannot penetrate the solid phalanx of lowered heads and horns. Their only hope of prey is to catch a stray calf.

Birth or hatching always takes place in the safest location the parents can provide, yet predators are seldom absent. All young animals, whether they are nestbound or travel with their mothers, have some instinctive response to danger. Usually they hide or "freeze," relying on camouflage, though some flee with their mothers. The safety of youngsters depends on their immediate response to the parent's alarm signal.

There are several ways an animal can defend its young from an enemy—by attack, flight, hiding, or deception. Large, powerful animals—bears, lions, rhinoceroses, and hippos—are well able to defend themselves and their young. The thunderous charge of a rhinoceros intimidates every kind of creature. Because the young rhino rarely leaves its mother's side, it is seldom in danger. The same is true of the hippo youngster. Both mothers are grazers and remain with their offspring throughout the day.

But female lions and bears must go off to hunt; they leave their young concealed in a den or thicket. Newborn animals sleep or rest quietly, but older ones may be inclined to go exploring, and without their mothers present, this can be dangerous. Such youngsters are curious by nature, incautious, and incapable of effective defense.

Among large birds of prey, as among large mammals, adults are formidable enough to drive off any intruder. But for smaller birds, the careful concealment of the nest is the most effective form of parental defense. A lone songbird may attack a fox, but will probably not save its brood.

When massed in large numbers, however, small birds such as titmice, chickadees, and nuthatches are often successful in driving off large predators. The noisy, angry mobbing of many small birds cannot harm an owl, but it needs the element of surprise for its attack. The noise and confusion spoil its aim, so it flies elsewhere to find a meal.

Small mammals such as mice and rabbits are secretive in their comings and goings. These burrowing animals forage for food only at night, or at dawn and dusk, thus ensuring that the burrow does not attract attention. The rabbit doe leaves her newborn kittens asleep in their cozy pocket in the sod, concealing it with a coverlet of grass. She returns only once a day to feed them. The kittens have no alternative—they must stay safely where the doe left them.

Disturbed by a lynx, a white-tailed deer nudges her fawn into a hollow, where it lies perfectly still until she returns. She limps pitifully away, attracting the attention of the big cat in a "distraction display." Once clear of the area, she quickly abandons her deception and bounds off to safety. Later she returns to her fawn, which remained motionless in response to her signal.

The deer's performance is similar to the broken-wing display used by many birds. A killdeer mother, disturbed by a predator, gives an alarm call. Her chicks immediately flatten themselves against the ground and remain motionless and silent. She flutters away, just beyond the teeth of the enemy, while her mate reconnoiters, assembles the chicks, and leads them to safety. Meanwhile, the female skims gracefully away across the fields, leaving her frustrated foe to hunt elsewhere.

Keeping Young Out of Harm's Way

Camouflage is one of the most common forms of infant defense in the animal kingdom. What human beings see is not a reliable guide to the conspicuousness of a particular creature, for its enemies may be color-blind to the contrasts that are apparent to us. However, a predator can always see movement. The defense of many youngsters is to remain absolutely motionless when threatened. The adults of a few species take advantage of the fact that an injured animal is easy prey, and make great show of being disabled. A deer may limp pitifully until a cougar is far from its fawn, then suddenly put on speed. When ruses fail, even a defenseless parent may attack an enemy.

A prowling lioness bypasses a tiny Thomson's gazelle fawn, unaware of its presence. The infant escapes detection because it is almost scentless at this age, well camouflaged, and has an instinctive "freezing" response to danger.

The rabbit is one of the most vulnerable of small animals, and yet the mother is a staunch defender of her young. An enemy is roundly thumped by her powerful hind feet, and she often forces a retreat.

One wing dragging, the other up like a flag, *a killdeer screeches in "distress." The mottled chicks vanish into the grass as their parent lures an enemy away. Once the chicks are safe, the killdeer "recovers" and flies out of reach.*

A black skimmer chick disappears *as it wedges itself into the fork of a shore plant. The young of this species are active in their own defense. If there is no cover, an alarmed chick scoops out a shallow pocket of sand and holes up.*

Fetching and Carrying Young

At first, young nestbound birds and mammals are docile and relatively inactive. But as they grow older, they become venturesome. Full of curiosity, lured on by new sights, sounds, and fascinating smells, they stray from nests, burrows, and their mother's side as she moves around feeding or pauses to rest or groom.

Newborn shrews are not well coordinated, so their mother carries any stray infants back to the nest in her mouth. By the time they are eight days old, shrews wander extensively. Their mother periodically collects them by forming a caravan; each youngster firmly grips in its mouth the flank of the body ahead of it. After about eighteen days, the young are able to return to the nest by themselves.

The maximum distance a young animal may wander from its mother or the group is the social distance. When the youngster goes beyond the social distance, it is retrieved. At first, retrieval is chiefly the responsibility of the mother, though the young of some species do cooperate. Precocial young, imprinted on a parent, have a strong tendency to keep close.

Every young animal must learn the social distance of its species. Should it run ahead, its mother runs too. Without this "magnetic" system there would be no families.

Staying together is tremendously important for animals that aggregate in enormous herds at migration time. Every year, caribou travel hundreds of miles between summer and winter feeding grounds. Among such vast numbers of their own kind, a separated cow and calf would have great difficulty finding one another. Security lies in keeping together at all times.

A grouse chick wanders, drawn on by a flitting insect. Its attention should have been focused on the hen's calls, but the chick is diverted by this new curiosity. Finally alarmed, the chick calls in distress. The mother quickly gathers the rest of her brood and fusses along to retrieve the stray. If the hen had moved too far off, she would not have heard the cry of her chick. Contented by the presence of the rest of the brood, the grouse hen would not have perceived that one was missing — for animals do not count. Then the plaintive distress calls might have attracted a hawk or fox.

Some animals keep track of their infants by toting them along. Young wood rats firmly grip their mothers' teats with specially adapted incisor teeth and toboggan along the ground. But few animals are better equipped to transport infants

A herd of elephants may string out as they troop off to a waterhole, but individuals are little more than a trunk's length from neighbors. Maintenance of "social distance" is a universal characteristic of herds, flocks, and bands.

A mountain goat kid looks where it's going as the mother shepherds it over a ridge in Jasper National Park, Alberta. The sure-footed young can jump within a half hour of birth, but must stay close to a parent for protection from eagles.

A sprightly trio of warthogs gallops after the mother. An adult warthog can run at speeds up to thirty miles an hour, and an ordinary canter is likely to be brisk. However, if her offspring fall behind, the female goes back for them.

than the marsupials. Head first, a young euro, or red kangaroo, tumbles into the pouch when danger threatens or when it is tired and hungry.

Each female kangaroo or wallaby usually has two youngsters, a large joey that hops along behind her, and a small infant living within her pouch. When a new embryo reaches the pouch, the mother drives off the eldest of her three offspring and prevents the evicted middle-sized joey from climbing back into the pouch. From then on the joey must follow its mother, but it is still allowed to put its head into the pouch to nurse. Koalas also carry their infants in a pouch. As the young koala grows, it begins to ride on the mother's back, leaving her paws free to climb.

Troops of Barbary apes in Morocco move freely over their range, pausing to rest in the heat of the day, or spreading out to feed, protected by young males on "sentry duty." A young Barbary ape is born furred and button-eyed, but unable to walk. When its mother travels, it clings to her belly. Eventually it will change to the "jockey" position and ride on her back.

Social distance is not constant, but increases as the young grow older. For the first few days after birth, a moose cow remains close to her calf as it rests in thick cover. From the fourth day, the calf follows her, staying within a few feet. The cow teaches her youngster to "heel" by moving slowly enough for it to keep pace, or waiting for it to catch up.

Should the calf become too venturesome or inattentive, the cow disciplines it by moving forward and standing quietly among the bushes, waiting. Soon the calf becomes alarmed and seeks her, but she offers no help. These little adventures in

A female kangaroo gives two kinds of milk from different mammary glands. The new embryo in the pouch receives a thin fluid, while her older offspring—recently evicted from the pouch—is nourished by creamy milk, high in fat.

In early infancy, a baboon clings to the fur on its mother's belly when she walks or climbs. From the fourth to the seventh month, it rides her back jockey-style. If she runs, the youngster flattens, hanging on with all fours.

being lost soon train the calf to keep close. After a while, the young moose responds immediately to the head-nodding signal that its mother uses to retrieve it.

From three weeks on, the calf becomes more independent and wanders farther away, usually staying within sight of the mother. By the time it is three months old, the calf has a wide area around the cow for its activities—playing, chasing, and nibbling herbs and tender leaves.

The calf, which is never left alone for long, is attracted by other animals and will follow them indiscriminately. The cow's constant vigilance and the well-developed signaling system that exists between the two are the youngster's chief protection. When approached by wolves, the cow sends her calf ahead and is ready to defend the rear.

An infant langur monkey is frequently frus-trated by a recurring dilemma. Safe in its mother's arms, it watches the older infants and juveniles at play. They repeatedly try to lure the infant langur away from its mother's side. The infant is ready to play but its mother is not ready to agree. She restrains it—often by holding its tail.

At one month, the young langur toddles away unsteadily to a distance of five feet from its mother. By ten weeks, this distance has doubled. By three months, the young play together in groups while the adults rest or groom each other.

As they mature, young monkeys retrieve them-selves, returning regularly to greet or make contact with their mothers before turning away once again. The females no longer carry or lead the stragglers back, but use calls or signals. The "silly grin" that a rhesus monkey mother gives her youngster is a powerful retrieval signal.

A Mother-Infant Tug of War

As a young primate grows, it becomes increasingly venturesome. How far its mother will allow it to go depends on the species and the age of the infant. At two weeks, a rhesus monkey is permitted to explore up to twelve feet. Beyond that, it is yanked back. A gorilla infant doesn't reach ten feet until it is four months old. As the young gain distance, they are also allowed to stay away longer.

Rhesus monkey Langur Baboon Gorilla

1 month 5 feet

2 months 10 feet

4 months

2 weeks

15 feet

20 feet

8 months

4 months 5 months

1 month

Hitching a Ride

A litter of wood rats hangs onto the teats, bouncing and tumbling as the female runs. Their teeth are adapted for grasping and cause no damage. This kind of transport is used by only a few small mammals.

It is often necessary for a parent to tote its offspring away from an endangered nest, or to retrieve a wanderer. Some adults call, shove, or nudge; others snatch a mouthful of loose infant fur and run. But for many youngsters, a parent's body may be a temporary residence—combining all the advantages of a portable fortress, warm hearth, and lunch counter. Such a passenger has one main occupation—feeding.

Too young to follow its mother, a lion cub is hauled off by the scruff of the neck. A lioness conceals her young in a thicket while she hunts. If she discovers other animals nearby when she returns, she is likely to move her brood.

Marsupials have an effective means of keeping their young under surveillance: An infant is kept in its mother's pocket. Wherever a female tree kangaroo may travel, her infant goes along, sightseeing in safety and comfort.

Grebe parents take turns riding their chicks around. The young are firmly anchored in the adult's feathers, so that if a parent dives to evade an enemy, the chicks get dunked too. Sometimes one pops to the surface and must be reclaimed.

The female giant anteater of South America gives birth to a single offspring, which stays with her for about a year. The youngster drapes itself over her back as she wanders, and is protected from predators by her long, sharp claws.

In a moment of unusual tranquility, eight lion cubs line themselves up on a rock ledge. One adult lioness baby-sits while the youngsters' mothers are off hunting. The pride is a cooperative, extended family, where prey is shared, and the responsibility for protecting the young and rounding them up when they wander is a general adult concern.

Baby-sitting isn't a human invention. Many animals leave the kids with a sitter

At times, mothers must leave their young while they seek food or water. In herds and colonies, a pattern of behavior that might be called baby-sitting is sometimes evident.

Late in winter, the sprawling plains of northern Australia are parched in the hot sun. One by one the waterholes dry up; water buffalo cows must walk farther each day in search of water and good grazing. At first, they are accompanied by their calves, which were born in midsummer during the monsoon rains.

The rank, dry grass is poor nourishment for the cows, whose nursing calves make heavy demands on their water reserves, and their milk sup-

ply wanes. Soon the calves lack the stamina to follow their mothers across the dusty plains to drink. Then the buffalo calves are left behind in a "crèche," or infant group, while their mothers search for food and water. One or two cows remain behind, baby-sitting. Without this protection, the calves would fall prey to dingoes, the wild dogs of Australia.

Shorthorn cattle that are kept in the same region also use crèches in the same way. This is surprising because their ancestors, bred for centuries in well-watered Britain, showed no such behavior. This form of infant care is probably an ancient heritage of the species, dormant when not needed, but revived in response to the challenge of a harsh environment.

The Cape hunting dogs of Africa form a crèche for the pups of two or more females when the pack is off hunting. Usually, it is the females that baby-sit. Like wolves, Cape hunting dogs feed the young first, regurgitating part of the kill when

A greater flamingo adult marshals a flock of sooty gray, month-old chicks. Although the young birds are able to sift tiny water creatures from the lake, they are still fed for a time by both parents. One adult can protect a "crèche" of thousands of chicks, for only a few predatory birds can hunt the forbidding alkali lakes where flamingos breed.

they return from a successful hunt. The baby-sitters are also given food. Or the young may be led to a kill and allowed to feed before the adults.

Flamingos leave their chicks in enormous crèches while they are away feeding. A lone adult may be seen amid thousands of massed young. Penguin chicks collect in large fuzzy groups, with a few adults in attendance, while most of the adults are filling their crops with fish to bring back to their youngsters.

No one knows how the baby-sitters are selected, or select themselves. They are alert and responsible, fierce in the defense of their charges, shepherding them away from danger and rounding them up when they stray.

Some species do not have specific baby-sitting behavior, but their young are well protected nevertheless. Even when most of the adults in a gull or tern colony are away feeding, a few parents are present and they will attack any intruders. Thus the chicks are almost as secure as they are when all their parents are at home.

There seem to be as many ways for animals to protect their young as there are species. Whatever the system—the male Galápagos sea lion herding back a group of young frolicking too far from land, or the instant response of a whole chimpanzee troop to the distress cry of an infant—the young in families have a shield from danger, a time to develop.

Play, Practice, and Independence

The noisy, enthusiastic antics of young animals are fraught with peril,
for they attract the attention of enemies. But play they must,
rehearsing their adult roles for the stern time of testing that lies ahead

With lightning speed, three young otters leap out of a brook, up a muddy bank, then without an instant's pause, toboggan down the slippery bank into the water again. Over and over the game is played with acrobatic flourishes.

The mud slide, which the otters created themselves, entertains them for perhaps half an hour until, catching sight of a fish glinting in the water, they splash off after it. But the fish disappears seconds later, so they gallop ashore again and explore a hole in a fallen tree. The log is hollow, and they scoot in and out of the openings, chasing and colliding with one another.

The otter has been called the clown of the animal kingdom because of its dedication to play. But many other species play, and the activity is not exclusively juvenile: wolves, porpoises, otters, and many others play throughout their lives.

Some play is easily recognized, especially the romping of kittens, pups, cubs, fawns, and calves, which most nearly resembles the play of children. But sometimes it is difficult to say just what is—and isn't—play in animals. Because most bird behavior is highly ritualized, their play is especially hard to identify.

Play is infectious; the sight of others playing is an almost irresistible invitation to a young animal to join in the game. An animal at play is characteristically eager, excited, and totally absorbed in what it is doing, but the game has a "not real" element. A race among young hoofed animals has no finish; for no apparent reason, but with undiminished zest, the players suddenly switch to a game of tag. Fights may appear furious, but claws are sheathed, bites restrained, and kicks fail to connect. At any point, the pursuer may become the pursued, or a youngster may quit to seek its mother to nurse. Its defection may be ignored, or it may be teased or chased until the game is resumed.

An animal will play only after its primary needs are satisfied; it cannot be drawn into a game if it is cold, hungry, frightened, or sick. An adult animal, a dog or cat, that is usually ready to play cannot easily be enticed into playing when it is pursuing a prospective mate. Play occurs after the individual's needs are met and it is feeling well and energetic. Play is considered by some to be a means of expending surplus energy, and by others as a "drive" in its own right—on the same order as a hunger drive, or a drive to mate, but having a lower priority in the animal's life. It can't be described as something animals do for the "fun of it" because no one knows what fun is for an animal.

Intrigued by a porcupine, a ten-month-old cougar prepares to attack. Its first pounce is likely to result in a paw full of barbed quills, a painful lesson in porcupine-hunting. In time, the cat learns deftness in flipping the animal over on its back, exposing its unprotected undersides.

Play Fight, Real Fight

Play can be dangerous because it attracts attention. Very young animals are not likely to play except when a parent is present and providing some defense. As lion cubs or raccoon kits grow and develop some independence, they play among themselves while their mother is away. That play exists despite the risks involved underlines its importance in the life of young animals.

Certainly play develops the coordination and breathing power of young animals. Lungs expand —great gulps of air are sucked in to supply straining muscles. Long before the individual's strength is tried in earnest, it has rehearsed in its antics the activities of adults. Play is more than exercise, it is experience.

The types of play are obviously related to the animal's way of life. Predators play at hunting—

A four-way fracas becomes so tangled that bites and swats come from every direction. Sham battles develop the tiger cubs' strength and timing, so that by the time they are two years old, they are ready for life as solitary hunters.

a tiger cub blunders toward an equally uncoordinated littermate, missing it completely. In a matter of weeks, the young hunter is able to nab its victim with fair precision. All young cats engage in ambush behavior—crouched low, hindquarters tense, tail lashing, they charge and snatch at littermates, as in later life they will attack prey animals.

Prey animals, on the other hand, generally engage in escape play. The little ground squirrel, which is often food for flying predators, such as hawks, scampers to and from its burrow.

The Thomson's gazelle has a large number of enemies: cheetahs, jackals, lions, leopards, hyenas, hunting dogs, and eagles. It relies on swift flight for survival; not surprisingly, the playing of young "tommies" is mainly running.

One tommy fawn starts running in a zigzag path through the herd, and others follow the leader. Frisky as lambs, they may begin with a hop-hop-hop-jump gait, then "spronk," touching ground with all four legs rigid, tail and head held high. As the tommy pops up, its back legs are straight and the front legs flex in midair. On it goes, hopping, spronking, or galloping. Such chases, lasting a few minutes, end as abruptly as they began.

When a red deer calf plays, it runs to the top of a hillock. Rising up on its hind legs, it invites other calves to play "King of the Castle." Each calf attempts to shove the occupant off and hold the hill for itself.

Whenever two or more young animals live together, they fight among themselves; these may be real fights or play bouts. The interesting thing is that the animals seem to know which is which. When a month-old wild chicken suddenly runs at another chick, neck outstretched, its feathers ruffed like an Elizabethan collar, a real fight is in the making. The victim of the attack meets the challenge—backward and forward they spar, leaping to strike with non-existent spurs. Finally, one chick turns and flees, or gets pecked on the head. This fight is one of many bouts that will ultimately determine the rank of an individual chicken in its adult life in the flock.

Another time, a chick may run in an irregular circle, flapping its wings, before it takes a fighting posture in front of another chick. Again, the two chicks charge and strike, but this time the fight ends differently. One of them simply walks away, or turns aside to preen itself or feed. It was a mock battle that ended without settling anything.

The preliminary flapping-run gave the message to the other chick that "this is play." The rearing up of the red deer calf did the same, and no kicks touched its opponents. The laughlike panting of a chimp announces that it wants to play. Even if the playing gets rough, an animal feeling some pain does not respond with real hostility; the play signal keeps the hassle on the level of a game.

A play signal not only tells others that the challenge is not serious, it is also an invitation. By crouching and scampering, a puppy—or an adult dog for that matter—invites its master or another dog to romp. The dog wrestles and growls, but its jaws do no damage.

The greatest variety of play is found among the animals usually considered most intelligent: the primates and carnivores. Play seems to be essential to their normal development. In laboratory experiments young rhesus monkeys were reared entirely apart from their mothers. The original objective was to produce monkeys for research purposes in a healthy environment, free of disease, where scientists could gain access to the infants without having to fight an alarmed mother every time a youngster was weighed or examined.

The result, however, was that though healthy, the young animals grew up to be social misfits—fearful, sometimes neurotic to the point where they gnawed on their own bodies. In adult life, they were incapable of normal sexual behavior. The conclusion was that maternal deprivation did irreversible damage to the young.

A further series of experiments was conducted where young monkeys were isolated, but allowed to play with similarly reared youngsters for only twenty minutes a day. Even such a brief "recess" seemed to compensate for the absence of a mother, and the monkeys grew up as well-adjusted adults, resembling in no way the totally deprived animals.

An Invitation to Play

Members of the dog family—wolves, foxes, coyotes, and domesticated dogs—have a common signaling system that notifies others when they want to play. The lowered forequarters, eager expression, and preliminary scampers avoid provoking a violent reaction from an intended playmate. Play signals are often a mild form of aggressive behavior. The mouth is open, and the teeth show, but the muzzle is not pulled up fully and the fangs do not seem menacing. The advantage of play signals is that the animals do not engage in any unnecessary bloodshed.

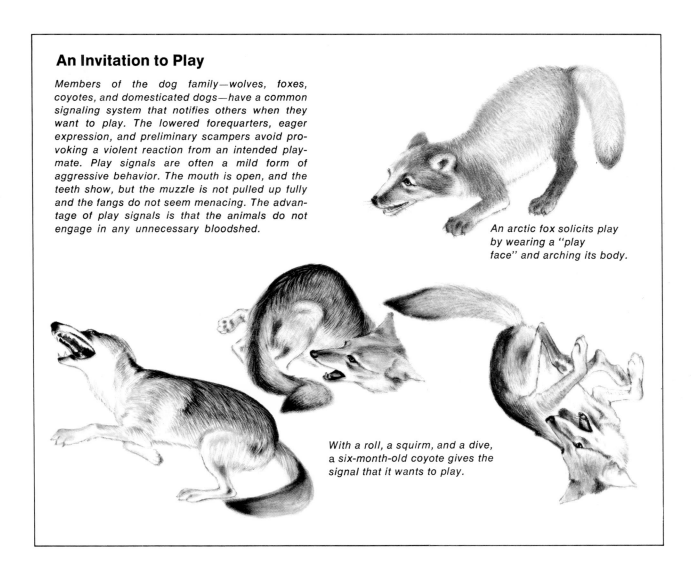

An arctic fox solicits play by wearing a "play face" and arching its body.

With a roll, a squirm, and a dive, a six-month-old coyote gives the signal that it wants to play.

A lion cub's needle-sharp teeth produce a show of annoyance in a young lioness. Adults are tolerant of cubs, but there are limits. When the youngsters wear out one adult playmate with their nonsense, they go on to pester another.

The world is a fascinating gymnasium where young animals climb, sniff, chase, scramble, and fight to the point of exhaustion

It seems safe to say that play fosters both the individual and social development of young animals. With each new life, a nervous system is turned on that begins to register myriad sensations—light, sound, scent, and texture. Day by day, the information is filed and sorted out in the young brain until a picture of the world emerges.

As a young animal begins to play with other youngsters, it receives a flood of new information. In fights, chases, and other games, it tests its new-found strength and develops skills. But more than this, it develops strong relationships with its playmates. Just as the bond between the young animal and its parent is the basis of a well-knit family, the bonds that are built during play are the beginnings of the social coordination that keeps herds and troops together.

Parents often play with their offspring, and indeed they may initiate many of the games. When a lion cub comes to greet its mother, she may tumble it upside down with her paw and begin to wrestle with it. Or she may twitch her tail in an enticing way and flee when the cub tries to attack it. When she leads her cubs into the pride, their social world expands suddenly and they find new playmates of all ages.

The male lion has a tuft on his tail that is highly attractive to cubs. The tuft is ambushed, captured, and chewed on whenever available. This appendage is such a perfect plaything, it seems to have been designed by nature as a toy for cubs.

A moose calf is solitary with its mother for three months. She becomes the object of the calf's games. Feinting and dodging, the youngster attempts to involve its mother in play.

Three weeks after birth a mother elk brings her calf into the female herd, and into contact with other calves. Gradually the calves come together,

A nine-month-old grizzly bear cub meets a striped skunk in a mountain brook and is suddenly jarred by a blast of scent. Like many other youngsters, the cub learns about skunks the hard way. Even adult grizzlies give skunks a wide berth.

and play begins. Chases soon occupy much of their time, interspersed with mock alarm signals—a high-stepping gait or a freezing posture.

As the time approaches for migration to higher ranges in summer, the mother elks lead the chases into shallow water. The calves seem fearful of water and must be lured into it at first, but they soon overcome their reluctance and eagerly splash in. This is important training, for on the way to higher ground, the calves will have to cross many rivers and streams.

Some play is directed at sham prey such as fluttering leaves. Twigs, stones, and pools of water are highly attractive to the young of many species. Raccoon kits insert their paws into every crevice, investigating endlessly. Presented with a crayfish by their mother, they often seem more interested in playing with it than in eating it.

Play and exploration are difficult to separate as aspects of a young animal's behavior. Play introduces a youngster to new places and things, and as it explores, it plays with whatever it finds.

Sometimes the new object is an animal of a different species. The cougar cub sees an interesting black and white creature bustling along. Naturally, that is worth a closer look. The object in question, a skunk, is wary of large animals and hurries away. No cougar cub could pass up anything so fascinating, so it follows. When it gets too close to the skunk, the youngster learns one of the most malodorous lessons of the wild: it is practical to leave skunks alone.

Occasionally, juveniles of different species strike up brief play relationships. Baboon and chimp young play tag with one another through the grass and into trees, swatting and dodging, but they soon separate. In one instance, however, a lonely young chimp was observed cavorting with a young baboon at times over a period of several months. Their play went beyond the usual chasing of mixed groups of apes and monkeys, and included wrestling, with the ticklish chimp chuckling as the two rolled over and over in the grass.

The unusual friendship ended because the baboon, like all monkeys, matured earlier than its chimp playmate. Then too, though the animals were the same age, the still-juvenile chimp far outweighed the baboon.

The Game
Never Ends

A puppy making rags of its master's slipper and a young monkey teasing another both exhibit an essential characteristic of play—the animal feels well. It is not sick, cold, hungry, or frightened. In early infancy, the young do not play when alone. But as youthful energies surge, they cavort while their parents are away. They gain strength, endurance, and skill in play, and their activities lead to wider exploration. Animal parents often seem annoyed by the exuberance of the young. Discipline is mainly negative—a nip or a swat—but a mother chimp is likely to distract her offspring with food. Either way, minutes later a new game starts.

A young baboon bounces on a branch, giving vent to high spirits. The youngster is at an age when adults do not try to coax it down; if it falls, it falls. In later life, nimbleness learned in play may save it from foes.

The play of young skunks mimics the defensive behavior of adults. Stomping their feet, they throw their tails over their heads in threat. They don't resort to chemical warfare; the play bout ends in wrestling.

Placid adult sheep endure the high spirits of the frisky lambs, which leap high in the air and often land on a broad, woolly back. Another lamb may follow the leader, and if the first won't get off, the game may become king of the hill.

After a "kiss" of greeting, by which prairie dogs identify one another, a pair of pups begin to roughhouse. When they are older, this kind of sparring changes to mutual grooming.

The family legacy may be a birdsong "dialect," hunting skill, or an awareness that man is not to be trusted

In many species of birds, the ability to sing the songs—or give the calls—of the parent is inborn. Ring doves, domestic fowl, and many others need no instruction and can produce appropriate sounds whether or not they have ever heard adults of their own species. In brood parasites—cowbirds and European cuckoos—this instinctive knowledge is essential, for the young are never reared by their own parents. If they were not born with the vocalizations of cowbirds or cuckoos, they could not attract mates.

But for large numbers of species, learning plays a role in the development of song. Bullfinches must learn all of it; if a nestling bullfinch is reared by canaries, it sings the songs of its foster parents for the rest of its life.

In the wild, nestling chaffinches begin to sing in a soft, rambling way called "subsong." Soon they are able to produce "plastic song," which resembles that of the adult, but at first lacks the phrasing and stability of adult vocalizations. Not until the youngster is ten months old does it have the fully developed song of its species.

When young chaffinches were reared in isolation, it was discovered that they could arrive at the intermediate stage on their own, but without hearing adult chaffinches, their songs never achieved the refinement and complexity common to normally reared birds.

The basic song of a species often has "dialects" of trills and flourishes that differ from one population to another. On the South American pampas, one species of sparrow has three distinctive dialects; the flatland sparrows have one different from sparrows of the nearby Paraná River delta, and both differ from the dialects of those on the mountainside.

The young sparrows learn their songs before wandering far from their birthplace. The dialect becomes important when the female chooses a mate; she tends to select a male from among those that come from the "right side of the tracks." Thus the differences isolate the populations of each region at mating time; crossbreeding becomes unlikely. Isolation is the first step in the formation of a new species, and it preserves within

In a head-on collision, male bison calves rehearse adult behavior. Except for the incessant butting of calves and the fighting of adult males in the rutting season, bison are peaceful grazers. Still, millions were wiped out in the last century by firearms—which no animal can fight.

each group any adaptations the birds have made to local conditions.

The family is the only means by which the valuable experience of an individual animal can be transmitted to a new generation. One of the most important lessons that a young animal learns within the family is how to respond to danger. At first, it attends only to its mother's signals; a disturbance sends a lamb or kid scrambling to its mother's side, or if it is a monkey it may hop onto her back. Safe with its mother, the young animal can look out at the alarming situation and learn. Every species keeps its own safe distance from predators—or tries to. The flight distance of a gazelle from a lion is a lesson of vital importance.

In many species, the capacity to learn about danger persists into adult life. The water buffalos of northern Australia are normally placid, curious, and approachable. Unless startled, they will allow an intruder to come to about 100 feet of them. In areas where these animals have been intensively hunted, they have learned to fear man, and now flee at the sight or sound of a human half a mile away. Each buffalo calf responds to its mother's signals; like her, it stands for a moment, large mobile ears outstretched, eyes on the intruder. In an instant, both turn and flee.

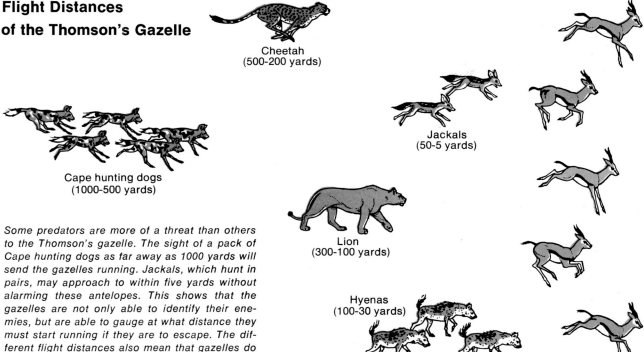

Flight Distances
of the Thomson's Gazelle

Cheetah
(500-200 yards)

Cape hunting dogs
(1000-500 yards)

Jackals
(50-5 yards)

Lion
(300-100 yards)

Hyenas
(100-30 yards)

Some predators are more of a threat than others to the Thomson's gazelle. The sight of a pack of Cape hunting dogs as far away as 1000 yards will send the gazelles running. Jackals, which hunt in pairs, may approach to within five yards without alarming these antelopes. This shows that the gazelles are not only able to identify their enemies, but are able to gauge at what distance they must start running if they are to escape. The different flight distances also mean that gazelles do not waste energy running when they don't have to.

This kind of learning has occurred wherever man has come with his rifle. Not every species has been able to adapt as well as the buffalo. The sea lions of the Galápagos and many other oceanic islands did not fear man. Having no other predators that approach by land, they were slow to learn the danger—though they are quick to flee from enemies in the sea. The sea lions stayed ashore and were slaughtered in untold thousands. The adults failed to learn that man was dangerous, so the young could not learn either; thus many populations of sea lions were decimated and some were totally wiped out.

The ability to learn about danger—as opposed to relying on instinctive responses—has great survival value for a species. For the sources of danger are ever changing, and an animal limited to instinctive behavior would not be able to accommodate itself to such innovations as man's modern hunting techniques.

For young predators, the skills of the hunt must be acquired before independent life is possible. When a grasshopper mouse kills an insect, it usually eats the head first, then the thorax and abdomen. When the young are ten days old, and for about six days thereafter, the mother leaves the abdomens of insects for the young to find and

eat. In this way they are given a taste for the prey that they must learn to hunt.

The European polecat female goes a step further. She carries her prey to the nest, then drags it out again, making a scent trail that the young must follow if they are to share her meal.

An otter mother catches a fish or frog, then calls her kits. She releases the prey for the young to recapture. They scamper excitedly after it, uncoordinated at first, later efficiently gauging the speed of the departing prey and intercepting it. It is by this means that the water-shy infants are led to water, thus learning two lessons at once.

Few young predators have more to learn than the big cats, for their prey is large and difficult to approach; it can generally be killed only by a bite on the neck that breaks the spine or strangles the victim. Tiger cubs are a year old before they join their mother on the hunt. She helps them make their first kill, dragging down a gaur calf or chital deer, and allowing the cubs to finish it off.

A cheetah may carry a young antelope to her cubs, then release it for them to chase. This behavior differs little from that of the domestic cat that brings a weakened mouse back for her kittens to "hunt." She, like the tigress and cheetah, assists only if the prey seems likely to escape.

Returning from a successful hunt, a fox vixen hides her kill, a pheasant, in the grass outside her den. Her yips summon the kits. The youngsters "discover" the concealed quarry—the first step toward hunting for themselves.

Parents do not set out to teach their young. Learning is mainly "monkey see, monkey do"

In a scrubby clearing, a young chimpanzee sits close by while its mother chooses a twig, makes a hole or enlarges an air hole in the side of a termite nest, and begins to "fish." She pokes the twig into the hole. The stick is immediately attacked by termites that are the defenders of the colony. Hanging onto the twig with their powerful pincers, the termites are withdrawn from their nest and are licked off the stick by the adult chimp. Her offspring imitates her, perhaps choosing a twig that is too large or small. Eventually the youngster learns by trial and error how to get these delicacies, and a new food is added to its diet.

The lessons of what to eat and what to avoid are essential to young vegetarian animals. Death can lie in the innocent-looking leaves or berries of a poisonous plant. In a troop of monkeys, the behavior of each member is observed by all the others. What a juvenile does is eventually seen and copied by its peers, but what a dominant male does all observe and imitate. Should such a male experiment with new foods, he might well lead his troop into a disaster in which he would die, along with many others. He is the repository of the experience of the group and must be conservative in feeding even when food is scarce.

Youngsters learn the food habits of the troop from their mothers and other adults. But they are venturesome feeders. Sometimes a juvenile tries a new food and dies of poisoning. This is unfortunate, but no tragedy, for the troop survives. This lack of caution, however, can be beneficial to the troop. Should the new food prove harmless, its consumption becomes common practice.

A group of young Japanese macaques were observed by scientists who lured the animals to the study area by providing sweet potatoes. It was the monkeys' custom to remove the sand adhering to the potatoes by rubbing them. When one youngster washed the sand off in a running brook, the practice spread, first among other juveniles, then to their mothers, and finally throughout the troop.

Beyond the lessons of survival—escaping from danger, finding appropriate foods, and learning to hunt—the family provides the young with social training of great importance.

The great-ape nursery is a favorite attraction in many zoos. An infant chimp, gorilla, or orangutan

A young baboon intercepts a leaf that another was about to eat. Plenty of leaves are available, but what one has, the other wants. The tendency to imitate is highly developed in primates, and results in a varied repertoire of behavior.

can be seen there in human nursery conditions— complete with diapers, bottles, and human nurses. The mother may be in a cage nearby, but she cannot be trusted to care for her offspring. Left in her hands, the infant would soon die, for she is hopelessly incompetent as a mother. She may seem puzzled by her infant's presence, or may fail to hold or nurse it. She usually loses interest quickly, which allows the keepers to hurry in and rescue the youngster.

Much of the behavior of these large, intelligent primates is not instinctive, but must be learned within the family. In fact, the whole social group contributes to the training of the young. In the wild, a young female ape plays with infants of other families, and lives with her own mother while she rears younger siblings. Thus the young-

ster is prepared for motherhood, and for all the other skills of adult life, by the example of others.

The usual way to capture great apes in the wild is to shoot the mother and take her infant; adult animals are too difficult to subdue and transport. The orphan is then brought to a zoo, where it grows up among humans. The youngster never sees the normal behavior of others of its species.

Thus, when a female captured in infancy matures and bears young (that is, if she is normal enough to breed), she is helpless because she has nothing to guide her. Her infant is too valuable to be left to die, and so another generation is reared artificially. If the infant is female, she too will most likely fail at motherhood. The cycle of parental incompetence is unhappy proof of the vital importance of a family to these species.

A Moose Calf Grows Up Alone with Its Mother

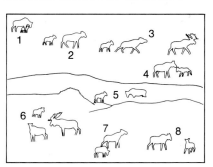

A moose calf is born in spring, well hidden in the woods (1). Soon after birth, the young animal learns to follow its mother (2). All animals, including other moose, are driven off; the mother signals the calf to fall back while she rebuffs the intruder (3). The calf attempts to draw its mother into mock fights and chases, but she is more an object of play than a playmate (4). The only time the two separate is when the mother feeds in deep water; the calf stays on shore (5). In the rutting season, a cow accepts the advances of a bull only if he is friendly toward her offspring (6). A calf stays with its mother through the winter (7), but as spring advances, a pregnant cow drives her calf away (8). When a new calf is born, the mother frustrates all the yearling's attempts to come near.

Elk Calves Live in a World Full of Playmates

Elk mothers give birth within a short distance of the band (1), and soon rejoin the group. When the females graze, the young are left in well-protected calf pools (2). Unlike the moose calf, elk youngsters have many playmates. Squealing and rushing, calves and cows play tag and engage in mock battles (3). The mothers lead chases into water, which frighten the young at first (4). Soon they splash in eagerly. The heeling response occurs later in elk calves than in moose, but it is well established by the time they migrate (5). In the rutting season, calves remain with their mothers, which are collected into harems by the males (6). Males and females join one herd in winter (7), and separate in spring. Before a new calf is born, a female drives off her yearling (8). Rejected young form roaming herds (9).

Many animals endure an awkward age—when they are too young for independence, but too old for parental care

When the family has fulfilled its function, it breaks up. The young, which have been brought to the stage of independence, either leave the family of their own accord or are driven away by their parents. Bonds are not broken by decision, but by behavior that increasingly chafes and strains the bonds until they break.

The feeding of young mammals, which is central to family life, is often the pivotal point in the breaking of family bonds. As the young grow and their demands for food increase, the mother's supply of milk—and ultimately her patience—is overtaxed. As the gap between supply and demand widens steadily, the ever hungry offspring pester their mother to nurse.

Huge blue-footed booby chicks—nearly as large as their parents—are still fed by both parents. The downy feathers of infancy stimulate parents to care for their offspring, even though adult plumage is beginning to show in back.

Some mothers withdraw to places where they are difficult to follow. But the young are agile, so new tactics are necessary: threats, snarls, or growls. The juveniles try harder, begging pathetically, only to be driven away with punishing swats or nips. The sequence is tedious and its outcome inevitable—the end of parental feeding and usually breaking of the parent-offspring bond.

Water buffalo bulls are responsible for the weaning of young males. The bulls form harems just before the calving season, and young males are chased away. Though the newborn calf has priority at the teat, the buffalo mother still nurses her yearling daughter—an animal that may be almost as large as the cow herself.

In societies where male and female live together year round, the young already have bonds with others, so that weaning, though distressing, does not mean a complete change in their way of life. The young baboon is prevented from nursing, or sleeping near its mother, but during the day, the mother will still groom her youngster; this has a calming effect during the trying days of the breakup period. The young are well able to feed themselves at this age.

The Importance of Appearance

Though weaning is important in the breakup of mammal families, it is not the only source of change. Physical growth of the young affects the behavior of adults. A young mammal or bird is not a small replica of the adult. The proportions of the head, body, and legs are often remarkably different, and the youngster's behavior is unmistakably infantile. As it grows and loses some of the characteristics of infancy, it loses some of its attractiveness to the parents.

Among some baboons, the conspicuous black coat of the infant is the key to a pampered life and solicitous attention from all the adults in the troop. But at the age of four to six months, the tan coat gradually replaces the black infant hair.

Although its behavior is still infantile, the baboon youngster experiences a drastic change in status: it becomes just another juvenile. Formerly attentive females become increasingly irritable when the infant approaches and may even attack it. The mother loses her favored position in the troop, and she too loses some of her interest in the young as she resumes her former status.

The misery of a rejected youngster is relieved by the company of its peers. Minutes after a young baboon has been cowed by the stare of an angry adult, it is usually off playing with other young.

Two young male bison park *on the other side of the road from the main herd. They are no longer tolerated by their mothers, which have just given birth to light-coated calves. They must also steer clear of the aggressive adult males.*

A rollicking band of baboon youngsters *tries to entice a black infant (center) into their games. The infant crouches in uncertainty with its back to the players. The adults watch every move; if the infant cries, the peer group is shooed away.*

Late in the breeding season, a white-plumed adult gannet lands in the thinning colony; many of the salt-and-pepper juveniles have flown or dropped from the cliff into the sea. The loss of unkempt downy feathers ends parental care.

As they grow, young animals change in color and form; their proportions and behavior begin to approximate the adults'. The soft, mottled coat of a lion cub gives way to the tawny pelage of the mature animal. Before its first winter, the mottled down of the laughing gull chick is replaced by the somber brown back, streaked breast, and banded tail of the juvenile; by the next spring, the young laughing gull has molted again and assumed its adult gray and white plumage.

Some infant coats have the benefit of camouflaging the youngster from predators, especially in species not concealed in nests and burrows. The young of most ground-living precocial birds—plovers, partridges, ostriches—have spotted or striped down in neutral colors that tend to "vanish" when they remain motionless. As the birds become mature, some lose their camouflage.

All the various changes greatly influence the behavior of the parents, who usually become increasingly irritable and finally hostile to young. At some point—differing widely from species to species—the bond begins to break.

Parents Also Change

Physical changes within the parent's body are always part of family breakup. The hormones that stimulated caretaking behavior gradually diminish, and are at a low point as the offspring approach independence.

In species where a second brood or litter is produced within a short time, the young of the first are most often well along toward independence. Rodent parents are likely to be especially intolerant of their earlier offspring. The hormones that induce parental behavior are present, but the stimulus that triggers care is the newborn young, not the older juveniles.

Songbirds in warm climates may hatch two or more broods of young during the spring and summer. As one brood fledges, the female incubates a new clutch, while the male takes over the feeding of the earlier brood. Only when the last brood is reared does the pair separate, or perhaps fly together into a winter flock.

Some tree-nesting young flutter down long before they are able to fly. Australian white-winged chough nestlings live on the ground for about two weeks, protected and fed by their parents. At first they are only able to walk, following weakly after the adults. They are fed for about two months.

When a young gannet first leaves the nest, it is not yet ready to fly. Wearing its speckled immature plumage, it makes its way through the colony,

A generation gap is apparent as two pelicans eye one another. The light undersides of the all-brown juvenile indicate that *it is less than* a year old. With every molt, its head feathers become lighter, its body darker. Pelicans are adult at two.

stalled frequently in its progress by the attacks of adult gannets past whose nests it must go. Vacillating and intimidated, the fledgling looks over the edge of the cliff to the churning waves below. The impulse to fly gains ascendancy and off it goes, landing anywhere from a few hundred feet to a couple of miles out at sea. From this time on, the fledgling is on its own.

Because it is fat, a young gannet finds it difficult to dive beneath the surface of the water. The buoyant fat is a reserve that nourishes the youngster until it learns the art of diving after fish.

A common pattern of separation is for the parent or parents to remain in the nest or burrow and to drive the young away. But abandonment is another form of rejection that occurs in many species of mammals.

Prairie dogs live together in "towns," comprising many families on separate territories. In each territory there may be two or three males and several females. While the young are being reared, the parents begin to dig burrows on a new territory at the edge of the town. Finally the adults depart, leaving the young in possession of the old territory, now overgrown with weeds. The young are on their own, but on familiar ground, with an established burrow system.

The volcano-like mound at the entrance of a prairie dog burrow serves not only to keep out surface water, but as a sentry post as well. Passageways leading to the rounded-out nesting chambers are about three feet below the surface, and generally have two or more exits. When a burrow fills up, the young inherit the homestead; adults move out.

Bear cubs take to the trees in play or to escape an enemy. Usually, a mother bear chases them up, keeping them out of the way while she deals with a foe. At ten months of age, a cub may descend only to find its mother gone.

A mother tree kangaroo boxes with her older joey while its younger sibling rests in the pouch. When the smaller one gets big enough to live outside, a new embryo takes its place. The boxing becomes serious—the eldest is rejected.

Young animals that are abandoned or rejected are generally well provided with fat to tide them over the difficult—and one can suppose disconcerting—period when they are left by themselves.

A grizzly bear mother, confronted with danger, chases her cubs up a tree to keep them out of harm's way while she deals with the enemy. When the time comes for mother and cubs to separate, she uses the same method. The cubs climb a tree, and she simply walks off, leaving them alone.

The full breakup sequence—from the beginning of parental rejection to the entry of the young into adult society—was studied on an island off the coast of Australia, where a population of domesticated chickens have reverted to life in the wild.

The feral hen broods her chicks at night in a hollow under a tree, apart from the adult flock. When the young males are about six weeks old, they begin to show the first signs of sexual behavior. When the hen sits, they attempt to mate with her. She discourages this by standing.

At night, however, when the hen broods her family, she cannot ward off the young males by standing and brood the rest of the chicks at the same time. After two or three evenings of disturbance, the hen climbs into a tree to roost.

An Anxious Time

The chicks become frantic. One by one they skitter up the trunk and out along the branches, fluttering from limb to limb. Frequently, a chick plops to the ground and has to start again. Eventually, they all reach the hen. Thereafter the family roosts in the same tree every night. Chickens invariably perform poorly in simple mazes designed by psychologists, but in their real world of trees and branches, they master a complex three-dimensional "maze" with ease and confidence in just one or two evenings.

During the day, the young males fight among themselves, and soon begin to threaten the hen. But her threats in return gradually inhibit them. At about eight weeks of age, the young of both sexes are no longer able to walk directly up to their mother. They must pause momentarily at about two feet, and turn aside before walking past.

As the hen increases her rejection of the brood, anxiety builds up. She becomes the center of attention, and the chicks seldom stray more than fifteen feet from her during this period.

When the brood is twelve weeks old, the hen leaves them to return to the cock during the day. The cue for her desertion seems to be the loss of the few remaining downy feathers from the heads

One eighteen-week-old chicken starts running, its flockmates follow, and a second juvenile flock streams along. As the flocks mix, they exchange pecks, then separate. Repeated streaming eventually brings about a joining of juvenile flocks.

of the chicks. They join her at night to roost, but her intolerance grows. At first they are pecked a few dozen times. By the end of a week, driven off by hundreds of violent pecks, the young give up. The parent-offspring bond is severed.

Although they are deserted, the chicks' way of life is not greatly altered. They begin to show an interest in socializing with other adults in the area, both male and female. They are invariably driven back whenever they approach, and soon learn chicken "etiquette," though they have not yet won a place in adult society.

Occasionally two abandoned broods converge. One or two males from each brood run out to spar with the strangers. No dominance seems to emerge from these bouts—they simply keep the broods apart.

Throughout life, chickens have a tendency to follow a running bird. At about eighteen weeks, a young male runs across a clearing and, as usual, his siblings follow. But this time the chicks of a nearby brood are drawn after him. A stream of running chicks flows across the clearing to a tree, then stops abruptly.

For the first time in their lives, the young birds find themselves surrounded by strangers. A few pecks are delivered, and the families separate. Throughout the next week, this occurs scores of times, about every twenty to forty minutes. At every meeting there are scattered fights, each of which settles another dominance relationship, until the separate broods are amalgamated into a single adolescent flock. In many brief encounters, the birds grow accustomed to one another and work out both male and female peck orders.

A week or so later, the combs of the males begin to show the bright red that marks sexual maturity. They leave the adolescent flock and become solitary wanderers at the edge of adult flocks.

Refuge in a Harem

Soon after, the pullets—young females—also develop bright-red combs. The young males return to court and chase after them. To escape their violent attentions, each pullet flees hither and thither, eventually entering the harem of an adult male, where young males cannot follow. The pullet squats down beside the dominant male—the normal approach of a stranger. At first the hens in the flock seem to ignore her. Not so the rooster; he courts and mates with her.

Once the pullet is accepted by the dominant rooster, she must establish relationships with all the other females in the flock. One by one, the resident hens threaten or peck her, and she submits to each. She is now a member of the flock, but the lowest female in the peck order.

Sexual maturity sets young males wandering; the development of combs on the pullets attracts the young males. The resulting harassment drives the young females into adult society. Thus, by a gradual process of growth—and the changing responses of others—maturity is thrust upon the young of both sexes.

A young ruffed grouse listens to the sound of a distant drummer—an adult male proclaiming his territory. Braced on his tail, the bird brings his wings down, forward, and up, producing a thumping noise that builds in frequency.

A young animal suddenly finds it must compete with its own parents for food and space

When the young animal is no longer able to turn to a protecting parent, the world at large commands its full attention. This is a period of severe trial for the youngster, which must become a part of the adult world by its own efforts. The animal becomes a competitor against all others of the species, including its parents.

There are three general patterns of life among the newly independent young. Some lead a solitary life; others join their peers in juvenile groups; the rest are already part of an adult group, where they remain while they grow up.

When the adults of a species are solitary, so also are the young. Juvenile bobcats, mink, deer mice, squirrels, and grouse on their own for the first time soon find that the suitable territories or home ranges are filled with residents. They must avoid not only predators, but the adults of their own species as well. Inconspicuous in behavior, the young find their food when the adults are resting, emerging to hunt at the least favorable times.

Something of the solitary way of life was learned by attaching tiny radio transmitters to the necks of male ruffed grouse in a forest in Minnesota. One was a first-year male without a territory. Every evening he threaded his way on a fairly regular course through and between the territories of six or seven resident males.

In the evening during spring and summer, each territorial male would "drum" from a particular fallen log or boulder within his territory.

One night a fox killed a resident male. Although at that moment the wanderer was a considerable distance from the dead bird's territory, before morning he had established himself on the vacant site and was booming out his presence.

The young ruffed grouse traveled a path that enabled him to eke out an existence while avoiding encounters with residents. He had learned to recognize their calls, so could quickly detect the absence of an owner and inherit his castle.

Many species find security in a flock of juveniles, where the group is alert to hidden enemies. Most small songbirds enter such flocks after they leave the family. The sparrow hawk hurtling down into a dense crowd of young birds is put off its aim by the confusion of their flight.

When young of both sexes remain in the group—

Some Youngsters Wander for a While

Adélie penguins arrive at the breeding colony for the first time at the age of two, but not till six do they become established breeders. Juvenile gray seals also have an unsettled period, when they wander far afield.

An immature Adélie builds a useless pebble nest. It may have found a mate, but the breeding season is over. Adults care for fuzzy chicks as juveniles wander around, often making a nuisance of themselves.

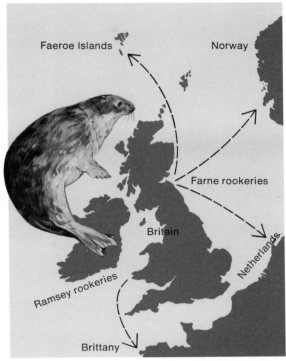

Faeroe Islands
Norway
Farne rookeries
Britain
Netherlands
Ramsey rookeries
Brittany

Adult gray seals stay near their rookeries, but the pups spend their first two years traveling. One pup tagged at Farne was found in the Faeroe Islands, another in Norway. Most probably do not go this far.

olive baboons and rhesus monkeys, for example—they are protected throughout the period of growing up. But in other species, young males are driven out of families to fend for themselves; female elk, red deer, Uganda kobs, and wild sheep remain in herds with their mothers. Young males take up life in all-male groups at the periphery of the adult society. This is the pattern for some monkeys as well—notably the gelada baboons and the langur monkeys.

Entry into the breeding group depends on rank, especially for the males. The young must usually climb the social ladder, but not all of them have an equal start. There is a social inheritance of rank that gives the young of dominant females a definite advantage.

The mothers of elk calves may assist them in their fight for rank. A dominant cow that enters the fray when her calf fights another will bring victory to its side, even though the other calf's mother is also helping.

The offspring of dominant female monkeys also have different social inheritances from the young of subordinate females. The young of dominant rhesus or macaque females remain at the center of the group even after weaning. When such a privileged juvenile fights with a monkey older than itself—an animal with obvious advantage—the high-status mother may intervene and help her youngster win. When danger threatens, the youngster is safe at the center of the group while low-status juveniles are vulnerable to predators at the outskirts. The privileged young therefore have the better chance to survive and reproduce.

Finding a Place in the World

Young animals enter adult society in one of three ways—by taking up a solitary existence, by becoming junior members of an adult group, or by collecting into "graduating classes" of the same age. The pattern is determined by species—the young adopt the same life style as their parents. The solitary young may separate from a parent gradually; a porcupine is weaned at seven weeks, but may associate with its mother throughout the summer. She forages near her single offspring, and does not reject it. Normal wandering brings about the breakup. Cats, on the other hand, drive their offspring away. For gregarious species, juvenile status often means a long apprenticeship.

Not quite ready to fledge, a juvenile osprey fans its wings at the edge of the nest. Independence, at about eight weeks of age, is a dire time for these birds. They must learn how to catch fish at once, or die.

A wind fluffs the soft guard hairs of a young porcupine, revealing its quills—which it is capable of using from early infancy. With this defense, and a willingness to try many foods, it is well armed for a solitary existence.

Speed, camouflage, and caution are the cottontail's defense against a host of predators. The high mortality is offset by impressive reproductive rates: A female has three to five litters a year, with up to seven in each.

Young male Uganda kobs are initiated into adult society by joining bachelor herds. The older members await a chance to claim a small territory—to which the females come to mate—but it is extremely difficult to oust a territorial male.

Growing up in bighorn sheep society is pleasant and playful. When a lamb is weaned, it picks another ewe to associate with —often an old, non-breeding female that willingly plays with it. Males stay in a female herd till three; then they join the adult rams.

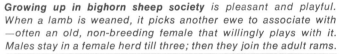

A juvenile flock of short-billed dowitchers gathers on mud flats to feed. The adults leave the young behind when they migrate. A month later, the juveniles follow in compact groups.

Disaster for one animal may be another's good luck. A kori bustard foraging near a savanna brush fire makes a feast of insects and other small animals driven from hiding by the advancing flames. When the fire nears, the bird can fly away.

The first year of life is the hardest. When natural disasters strike, the young are the first to die

Every spring and summer there is an enormous overproduction of young animals, yet when the breeding season arrives the following year, the number of adults entering the race to reproduce is approximately the same as the year before.

The harsh conditions of winter naturally have the greatest effect on the old and the sick. But experience is of great importance, too, and the mature fare better than the young. New at the trials of survival, only the strongest juveniles survive the ordeal of their first year.

In one population of gray seals on the Cornish coast of Britain, the death toll of seal pups runs to about 60 per cent in their first year. The pup is nursed for only three weeks, during which time its birth weight of about thirty-five pounds increases to approximately ninety-two pounds from the rich nutrients of the mother's milk. If the mother seal

dies or becomes separated from the pup in the crowded colony, the youngster may survive long enough to go to sea, but it will probably not have received enough nourishment to be insulated against the cold water. And it may not have the strength to find its own food.

The mortality rate among the seal pups may run higher than 60 per cent if the weather is stormy. Such losses are natural and inevitable—a part of the reproductive life of the gray seal colony.

Among birds, deaths occur even within the safety of the family. It is not unusual for half a brood to die before the young are fledged. The causes are many: predation, bad weather, scarcity of food, and disease. Once the birds are fledged, their death rate continues to be high throughout the perilous first year of life.

Red grouse males take up territories on the heather-crowned moors of Scotland in September and early October, and hold them—with minor boundary changes when breeding starts in April—until the following August when the young are reared. The red grouse is unusual in that the young males have about the same chance of securing territories as do the older, more experienced males. Sexually mature young males usually pass through

Arriving at a dried-out waterhole, *springboks, zebras, and a lone giraffe search for traces of water. Thirst and hunger take a heavy toll of grazing animals when drought strikes the African plains. Predators make short work of the weakened animals.*

a waiting period before they can gain a territory or the high status necessary for mating.

In any year surplus grouse, mostly the young, wander through the territories, attacked any time they are observed by the landlords. Silent, furtive, persecuted, they live a marginal existence.

The grouse that does not gain a territory in the fall usually is dead by spring. In the hunting season, the grouse that fall to the sportsman's gun are these surplus birds. In a large hunting area, scientists who tagged all the grouse found no territorial birds among the hunters' kills. Evidently, the security and cover of a territory are a tremendous advantage to the holder, protecting it from human hunters and such natural predators as foxes and hawks. But it has also been found that when disease sweeps the grouse populations, fewer territorial birds die. Both classes of birds may carry the same number of parasitic worms, but more surplus birds than landholders will be killed.

There seems a paradox in this situation. The young emerge from their families in the pink of condition, carefully nurtured and reared by attentive parents, yet within a year most of them are dead. Inexperience in dealing with dangers takes a heavy toll, but there is more to it than this.

A mother cougar stands aside *(left) as her ten-month-old cubs worry a deer carcass. The cubs themselves are unable to catch anything but small game. At one year of age, newly independent cougars must rapidly improve or starve.*

The body's defense system has certain limits. If pushed too far, the system backfires

When an animal is alarmed by a threat, suffers an injury, or feels the pangs of hunger or cold, it has a strong automatic reaction that affects every part of its body. The animal becomes alert and tense; it is prepared for the emergency by hormones secreted by its adrenal glands (small, paired glands located above the kidneys). The hormones speed up the heartbeat, increase blood pressure, and enable the muscles to work longer and faster. The keyed-up animal is better able to withstand stress.

The animal turns to face the alarm, perhaps to investigate more closely, but more commonly as a prelude to flight. If the threat is from an intruder, the response is to attack, or to defend itself. The alarm over, the animal's body returns to its normal physical condition.

But animals cannot flee from illness, injury, cold, or hunger. Nor can they always escape a threat if they live within a group. A monkey that is constantly persecuted by a dominant animal behaves submissively. The adrenal reaction may accompany each threat it receives, giving the animal the strength to endure what it cannot flee.

At first, the adrenal response is a powerful aid; the creature becomes physically stronger, able to tolerate bullying, and more resistant to diseases of all kinds: viruses, bacteria, and parasites.

But if the adrenals are repeatedly activated over a long period, their effectiveness diminishes. Now the animal is in trouble. What previously produced an increased resistance to stress now produces general physical weakness and greater susceptibility to disease.

The cumulative effect of stress is something like that of the waterdrop torture of a human being. The first drop is a trivial annoyance, but over a long period the repeated drops become intolerable; eventually they can kill the victim. In a similar way, the small but continual social threats in an animal's life become a destructive force. The animal is overtaxed, rendered susceptible to disease, and becomes an easy prey for its enemies.

The wandering red grouse male is constantly subject to stress. The ground he covers is never completely familiar and he is alert and tense. Feeding unobtrusively on the territory of another, he may at any moment be harassed by the owner and driven out. Flight alleviates the stress of one attack, but the fleeing animal is open to another when it crosses into the next territory. Exploring, feeding, fleeing—over and over—the outcast grouse is never at peace.

In birds, one of the milder expressions of stress

A rabbit takes off with a surge of energy sparked by fear. On familiar ground, the rabbit may slip into one of many hiding places. But in a strange area, only luck can save it. Repeated flight from a fox or dog overtaxes its body's resources.

White-tailed deer sprint *from the scent of danger. Wolves and cougars, their natural predators, have been reduced in number. The paradoxical result is that sick deer remain in the herd, overpopulation damages the habitat, and many die of stress.*

is the failure to lay eggs—or to nest at all. When a snowshoe rabbit is caught in a trap that does it no physical harm, the hormonal system may be over-stimulated in response to stress; death may result from "shock disease."

A study of muskrat populations in the marshes of Iowa set out to explore the role of their most significant enemy, the mink, in controlling musk-rat numbers. It was discovered that predation was not what held the population in check, but the organization of muskrat society itself.

Muskrats are aggressive territorial animals, quarreling among themselves and frequently in-flicting serious injuries—especially when the en-vironment is deteriorating. Mortality was found to be high among non-territorial muskrats, usually juveniles, and the various causes of death could be considered interchangeable. The stressed individ-ual is a candidate for death from whatever quarter the next assault comes.

While it is true that predation and hunting re-moves the weak and sickly from natural popula-tions, it is competition among the animals them-selves that largely determines which individuals will be weak and sickly. The mechanism is the social stress, which is produced within the indi-vidual animal's own society.

The red squirrel, *one of the most quarrelsome and active of rodents, is adapted to withstand a great deal of stress—territorial squabbles with other squirrels, fights with jays and starlings, and the attacks of a host of predators.*

Under natural conditions, animals do not eat themselves out of house and home

Only certain habitats will support a particular species of animal—grasslands for zebras, seashores for sandpipers. All habitats, whether plains, woodlands, thickets, rocky coasts, sandbanks, mountain slopes, or clumps of trees, have "carrying capacity." That is, even under the best of conditions, there are limits to the numbers of animals that can live off the land. Beyond this, the habitat suffers degradation. Drought or flood may diminish the resources of an area for a few seasons, reducing its carrying capacity. An overload of grazing animals, for example, results in cropping of the plants to the point where the edible kinds die out. The animals destroy their own habitat.

Over thousands or millions of years, communities of plants and animals have achieved a workable, and often fluctuating, adjustment of their numbers to the available resources. This adaptation of animals to their environment is something man is just now coming to appreciate.

When man kills off or greatly reduces the number of predators—the wolf, cougar, coyote, eagle— to prevent their attacking domesticated animals, other species are deprived of a natural population control. The overaged deer that would normally fall to the cougar's attack remains in the herd and diminishes the food supply. The large numbers of mice and ground squirrels produced annually may not be reduced in areas where birds of prey have been killed. Then the vegetation suffers.

Animals that have from time immemorial been controlled in part by predators are badly served when this control is lifted. Without the natural regulation of predators, prey animals proliferate, only to have their numbers controlled by harsher means—commonly food depletion and disease. Crowding produces hardship for all, even the strongest and fittest of animals.

Serious problems have also arisen where man has introduced an alien species where they have no enemies or natural disadvantages. Deer were brought to New Zealand, the mongoose to Hawaii, the gray squirrel to Britain, the starling, house sparrow, and pigeon to North America, the rabbit to Australia, and the muskrat to continental Europe. In every case, the spectacular spread and increase of these species have created a pest problem, for the animals did not evolve in their present

A cheetah hastily drags a gazelle to the thicket where she has hidden her young, some 200 yards away. Cheetahs kill more than they eat, for others often steal the prey. The bigger cats—even vultures—can seize a hard-won meal.

A predatory way of life offers no guarantee against sudden death. To find food for her litter, a female cheetah must necessarily leave the helpless kittens behind. Undefended, they are an easy meal for a lion, hyena, or jackal.

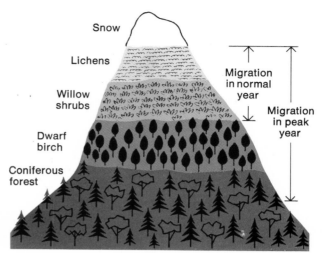

A Norwegian lemming rears back in a defensive posture at the sight of too many other lemmings. These rodents—a bit larger than a field mouse—have periodic population explosions. They are driven down from their lichen and willow habitats. But the boom is short-lived; unable to function normally under crowded conditions, many die from stress.

surroundings, and therefore lack important population controls.

Under natural conditions, fluctuations in animal populations do indeed occur. But an average taken over a long period shows that within certain limits most populations are remarkably stable. Fluctuations are most extreme among small vegetarian mammals; a lush spring may bring a rapid upswing in numbers of mice, rabbits, and voles. An increased number of litters and a higher survival rate contribute to the rapid growth of population. Their predators then also enjoy a high survival rate until a drought or other natural disaster occurs and the populations are cut back.

The Norwegian lemming has come to be the classic example of the boom-and-bust population pattern. But contrary to popular myth the overcrowded animals do not "commit suicide" by hurling themselves into the sea. The coats of these small rodents are water-repellent, and they swim quickly and well in the relatively calm water of lakes and streams. The fact that they test the current of a river, swim back to shore, and try again elsewhere—often quite a number of times—before striking out for the opposite shore suggests that they are attempting to survive.

Breeding beneath the snow through the winter, the lemmings periodically emerge in the spring in enormous numbers. The whole population becomes restless and the normally sedentary animals

move, each independently, up and down the mountain slopes. They meet, bark at each other, and separate. Each wave of lemmings triggers further disruption. They are so stressed by these encounters that they die easily in a fight, or while attempting to mate. Those that colonize the lower slopes dig new burrows, and drive away newcomers, but the arrival of still more lemmings sends them in a frantic search for space. By the end of the summer most are dead, leaving a few—mainly those that stayed behind—to recolonize the high country which is their normal habitat. The population then builds again.

The interesting thing is that the lemmings do not die of starvation when their numbers increase. Like other small rodents with boom-and-bust population patterns, the lemmings reduce their numbers by competition *before* the land is taxed to its fullest extent and the food supply is exhausted.

For lemmings, and for most other animals as well, the social system is the key to the regulation of population. A small increase in numbers produces only a few more outcasts or subordinate individuals, but a population explosion results in a breakdown of the whole social system. Then, weakened by competition and stress, many die from a wide variety of immediate causes.

Thus the ordeal of a young animal always takes place within the social framework of the species. Only the most capable and strongest survive.

Families in Society

*Millions of termites crowding a communal nest, all offspring of one
set of parents, form "superfamilies." Other societies are
made up of independent families, each minding its own business*

On long, narrow, nearly motionless wings, a herring gull rides the wind above a stretch of beach. Something in the surf attracts the bird's attention; it banks, turns, and dives in one smooth, fluid motion. As it swoops low over the water, the gull snaps up a morsel of floating carrion; then, taking advantage of a gusty updraft, the bird regains its former altitude with a few powerful beats of its wings. . . .

A ruby-throated hummingbird is suspended in midair as it sips nectar from a jewelweed blossom. After a moment, the bird backs away and darts to another flower. All the while the tiny creature's wings have been moving at a rate of fifty to seventy-five beats per second. . . .

Across the drifts of Antarctic snow, an Adélie penguin toboggans on its belly, propelling itself with its flippers. Arriving at a stretch of ice, the penguin stands and waddles like a windup toy; it never flies. In the water, the comic locomotion of land gives way to swimming, and the penguin glides through the water like a fish. . . .

The wings of the gull, the hummingbird, and the

*In plumed headdresses and frock coats, the crested
penguins of New Zealand mill about within the
confines of their messy colony. The pairs of birds
cease defending their small territories when
the fat chicks leave their nests. The isolation of
families gives way to noisy, amiable promenading.*

penguin—different as they are—evolved from an earlier, simpler form of wing. Every physical structure from the spine to the stomach has undergone this kind of evolution. Each has been gradually modified in many ways to serve the needs of survival in different circumstances.

Just as the physical structures of animals evolve, so too their behavior undergoes gradual change. The evolutionary starting point of family behavior was probably the parent-offspring bond, which arose independently in social insects, some fishes, birds, and mammals. In each of these groups, the basic parent-offspring bond was extended and other features of family life arose: bonds between male and female, and among siblings. In many species, social bonds have developed—relationships less strong than the original parent-offspring bond, but highly significant because they make possible the building of larger, cooperative societies.

A group of animals of the same species living together is not necessarily a family or a complex society. Herrings usually aggregate in huge schools, often numbering in the millions. There is organization in a school: the fish are regularly spaced and they all travel in the same direction, dispersing to feed and closing ranks when alarmed. When a school of fish turns, all of its members turn in nearly perfect synchrony.

But there are no bonds between fish in the school, nor do the members of the group attempt

A Group of Animals Is a Family . . .

What makes a family different from a simple gathering of animals is recognition of individuals. A fox knows her young, a moth never does. Many family animals spend part of the year without a family, in groups or alone.

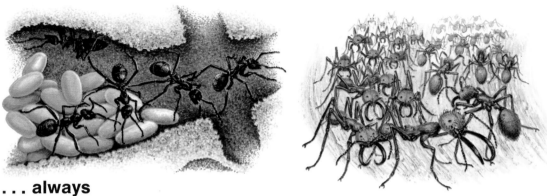

. . . always

Ants toiling in a nest are all members of one family—year round. But ant society does not depend on having a common home. Millions of army ants marching cross-country are also held together by family ties.

. . . sometimes

The family life of tree sparrows ends when the young are reared. The birds join winter flocks where relationships are casual. Chipmunk infants live with their mother for about three months, then shift for themselves.

. . . never

Many non-family animals exhibit some degree of social organization. One pine-procession caterpillar spins a thread and others use it to follow the leader. French grunts form schools that move with great precision.

to exclude individuals that join their ranks. Any other herring is a suitable neighbor, provided it is roughly the same size. Small schools readily amalgamate to form large ones, with an immediate loss of identity of the two groups.

An aggregation of animals becomes a complex society when some sort of individual relationships exists among members. Within a particular species of social animal, there are two kinds of individual, those in the bond and strangers; each is treated differently.

Sometimes, the existence of a society is masked by the scattered distribution of its members. Pairs of songbirds on territories in a woodland seem insular, but in fact they are part of the society of their species. Unmated birds are constantly scouting for entry into a family—ever ready to replace a dead member of a pair. Territorial neighbors communicate frequently and occasionally fight. Some species will gather to mob a predator, others will not. But pairs of chickadees or thrushes are very much a part of a society during the breeding season.

A puma making its solitary rounds in the hills of Montana is also a member of a society. Its solitary condition is the product of constant and elaborate communication: by means of scent, it warns others of its species to keep away. The fact that its food requirements necessitate a large home range does not mean that any puma is truly alone. It must meet, however briefly, with others of its species if the line is to be carried on. Thus societies are not limited to animals that stay together in herds, troops, or bands.

Superfamilies

Most families break up when the young separate from their parents. But in some species this separation never occurs. Instead the family grows into a larger society, the superfamily. Often the society grows within the nest of the parents, with the young remaining to assist in the feeding and care of future young. Old members die, new individuals are born, but the group as a whole remains relatively stable.

The social insects—ants, termites, and many bees and wasps—form superfamilies of this kind. The bond between members is the characteristic scent of the hive or nest. When one individual bearing the scent comes in contact with a nestmate, the scent serves as a badge of recognition. The absence of the scent on an individual is usually the signal for attack—and the intruder is either driven away or killed.

Insects are not the only creatures whose societies are centered in a communal nest. The kookaburra, whose wild, hysterical-sounding laughter awakens the Australian bushlands at dawn, also has a family pattern that might be described as a superfamily. This large kingfisher, sometimes called the laughing jackass, forms pairs—probably for life—and holds territories year round. The offspring of previous years remain in the family to assist with the new generation.

Each morning and evening the families assemble for laughing choruses, during which territorial rights are raucously proclaimed and the bond between family members is cemented.

With so many adults in attendance, the nestling kookaburras have a high rate of survival. Two to four white eggs are laid in the hollow of a tree; it is not unusual for all the nestlings to survive, though four in the nest hole may be a tight fit.

Kookaburras generally remain in the family into their third year. Sometimes a two-year-old

The sociable kookaburra usually hunts alone. It feeds on insects, but captures lizards, snakes, and small mammals as well. The bird kills a larger animal by knocking it against a tree, or by flying up and dropping it on the ground.

A Cape hunting dog female stands patiently as jostling pups eagerly nurse. The pups are cared for communally; all the mothers in the pack allow any of the pups to nurse. Thus a litter is likely to survive even if the mother dies.

will go off to find a mate, but this is the exception. Though these young adults are sexually mature, only the parents breed. The dominance of the parents seems to inhibit any attempts at breeding, or perhaps sexual activity in the young is suppressed in some other way. All the young eventually leave the parental nest—the males departing before the females—but the problems of establishing a new territory are great.

The suitable habitat is filled up, so territories are generally claimed only when one becomes vacant, from either the death or disability of the owner. The newly formed pair rears its first brood under difficult conditions, for the larger families of their neighbors encroach on the territory, extending their domains at the expense of the young pair. The second brood is easier to rear, for the pair then has the offspring of the first brood to aid in feeding the nestlings and in defending the family territory.

Communal nesting is also characteristic of the anis, kinds of cuckoos that are found in tropical America, and in Florida and southern Texas. The birds live together in flocks of a dozen or more members that build a single, dish-shaped nest of sticks, in which several females lay eggs. Both sexes share in incubation and in care of the nestlings. Maturing young remain with the flock, assisting in the care of the next brood, and perhaps also breeding the following season.

Communal Mammals

Mammals that form superfamilies are not attached to a particular nest site. Packs of wolves and Cape hunting dogs wander freely over their ranges, but in common with the kookaburra and the ani they retain offspring within the family.

The friendly, cooperative wolf family is similar in its basic elements to that of the kookaburra; only one pair of animals breeds, and the offspring

Under the watchful eyes of two adult baby-sitters, Cape hunting dog pups toddle around outside their burrow. Wanderers are easily retrieved; their white-tipped tails are like flags. As soon as the young are able to keep up, they join the hunt.

remain in the family beyond the age of sexual maturity. The two- and three-year-olds remain with their parents, joining in the hunt and sharing food with packmates.

The family life of the Cape hunting dog of the African savanna parallels that of the ani; more than one female produces pups. Individually, a hunting dog is poorly equipped to kill game, but in family packs they are among the most effective killers on the African continent. They do not use the lethal neck bite, as do the big cats; instead, they drag their prey to the ground and attack its vulnerable underside.

When these wild dogs return to the place where their pups were left, the hunters regurgitate food for the young and for the adult baby-sitters. This species is unusual in its care of the young, for when the pups are old enough to accompany the pack on the hunt, the adults stand aside and allow the youngsters to eat first.

Looking for a meal, a hungry pup licks the muzzle of an adult male. When the Cape hunting dogs return from a successful expedition, in late morning or evening, the adults regurgitate food for the pups and their nursery guards.

Colonies of blue-footed boobies are made up of independent families. This colony is spaced out on the floor of an extinct volcano on Daphne Island in the Galápagos group. Each family, including the chicks, attacks visitors.

A male jackdaw stood peacefully between two females that caressed his neck feathers. The first female failed to see the second when she sidled up. After a furious fight, the newcomer gained a mate, and assumed his status as well.

When animal families live in colonies, their conduct is anything but neighborly

In contrast with societies that build because the young remain within the family, other societies are formed when large numbers of individual pair families live together in cohesive communities. In these federations of families, there is bonding both within and among families.

Each year, vast numbers of arctic terns gather in breeding colonies on desolate, wind-whipped islands and coasts in the Far North. The male takes up a small territory, attracts a mate, and family life begins. At the edge of the colony is an invisible line, beyond which no nests are built. To the human eye, both sides of the line look the same, but not to the terns. If the population is large, the nest territories are smaller but the colony limits are constant. This mysterious boundary gathers all the families into a single unit.

Within the colony all are equal. Each pair has its own patch of ground on which it is dominant and from which it repels intruders. When an outsider, man or beast, enters the colony, the birds cooperate in mobbing the enemy. At other times, each pair leads an independent life, flying to and from the nests in a seemingly random pattern throughout the day. Families may squabble, but they also cohere, fenced in by tradition.

Not all social federations are as large as those of the tern. In smaller societies, the equality of each family unit may be replaced by a definite hierarchy. The jackdaw, a member of the crow family, forms flocks that have social bonds.

Jackdaw flocks are small enough so that each bird is able to recognize all the others. Strangers are mobbed by the whole group. When a man carries a black object in his hand, he will provoke the ire of a flock of jackdaws. Apparently the black object, particularly a drooping piece of black fabric, is interpreted as a dead jackdaw, and the man, therefore, as a jackdaw killer.

There is a peck order among male jackdaws, with the females assuming the same status as their mates. The unmated females also have a peck order. When a male of high status pairs with a female of low status, she immediately moves up the social ladder. All other females recognize her changed status and defer to her—even though the previous day they may have ignored or persecuted her. Such an elevation in rank sometimes turns

An adult prairie dog and three pups check for enemies as they leave the burrow, prepared to duck if they see a hawk. These gregarious rodents spend much of the time playing and grooming, and family members greet one another with a "kiss."

a meek and docile bird into an arrogant bully, constantly chasing and attacking the females that had formerly dominated her.

The peck order among families can be seen whenever the jackdaws aggregate in flocks. But on its own nest and territory, each pair is dominant, able to exclude all others.

Before the coming of the white man, the open grasslands of midwestern North America were dotted with the most spectacular of all mammal colonies—the prairie dog towns. When the animals were in their heyday, a single colony might spread across hundreds of square miles and comprise millions of individuals. Intensive extermination campaigns have drastically reduced their numbers, but a few scattered towns remain.

A prairie dog town is subdivided into family territories, usually of an acre or less. A typical family might consist of a male, three or four females, and a dozen or so offspring. No strong dominance order exists within the family.

There is little conflict between adjacent families of prairie dogs, for territorial boundaries are generally respected. And the presence of neighbors can be useful in times of danger—the first dog to detect the approach of a coyote or the shadow of a swooping hawk will emit a sharp bark that sends every family within earshot scurrying to the safety of its burrow.

When the family territory becomes crowded, the parents, rather than the offspring, depart. The adults move to the outskirts of town, establish themselves on a new territory, and set up housekeeping anew. Thus prairie dog towns, unlike the breeding colonies of seabirds, can continue to expand their borders.

FAMILIES IN SOCIETY 167

Three tailor ants use their powerful mandibles to hold the edges of a leaf together. The leaf, which becomes part of the nest, is sealed with silk that is exuded by the larvae. Other adults cart the larvae from seam to seam, as needed.

Many animals are specialists in certain jobs. Worker or warrior, each does the right thing at the right time

In most societies there is specialization of roles. In a small group, such as a pride of lions, roles are specialized by sex; the female is the hunter and the male is the protector of the pride. Though this seems to throw the greater burden on the females, the male's role is essential.

The larger the group, the greater the specialization. The largest societies are those of the ants, termites, and social bees and wasps. In each case, although there may be thousands or millions of members, the society is still a family, all individuals being offspring of the same female.

Because of the sheer number of individuals, division of labor becomes a necessity. The multitudes of termites in a nest could no more supply their own food needs on an individual basis than could human city dwellers.

The division of labor among social insects is rather like the various organs of a body, which are specialized for digestion, reproduction, and other functions. In termite societies, there are three major castes—reproductives, workers, and soldiers—differing in size, form, and role.

The societies of the common household termite of the eastern United States, *Reticulitermes flavipe* (yellow-footed net-patterned termites), are comparatively simple. Basically warm-weather creatures, these termites are inactive in winter, and thus cannot build nests and social structures as complex as those of tropical species. The temperate zone species generally nest in the soil, digging tunnels to sources of food.

Despite their destructiveness to man's wooden structures, termites are surprisingly vulnerable creatures. In most cases, their soft, fleshy bodies have only a thin, fragile coat of chitin, the horny substance that forms the external skeletons of insects. Termites need constant warmth and high humidity; they are utterly dependent on their nests. Outside, they dry out and die within a few hours, and most are defenseless against ants or other predators.

At the core of a termite nest is the chamber of the queen and king. They are the only sexually functional adults that remain permanently within a colony. In a small colony, the queen is likely to be about an inch long, perhaps five times as long as a soldier. Among the estimated 2200 species of termites there are tremendous variations in sizes and roles. But generally, the smaller societies have fewer castes.

Unlike ants and bees, termites have males and females in all castes. They are also unusual among social insects in having no larval stage. Termite eggs hatch into nymphs, or miniature versions of the adults. As they grow, nymphs periodically molt their external skeletons. Depending on the needs of the colony, nymphs may develop into workers, soldiers, or reproductives.

Chemical substances secreted by the queen and other members of the colony seem to determine the caste of the nymphs. The presence of these chemicals inhibits change, keeping the nymphs at an arrested stage. If the quantity of the substances emitted by one caste falls below a certain level, the inhibition is lifted. If, for example, many soldiers die, nymphs will develop into soldiers.

One of the most amazing termite societies is that of the *Macrotermes natalensis* (big South African termite). A well-established colony may number several million insects. The queen, housed in a special chamber, grows to gigantic size, up to five inches long and an inch thick. She is about 160 times larger than her mate, and 2400 times the size of a worker.

The house-wrecking termites of temperate climes are most often detected when the winged forms, which are specialized to start new colonies, fly out of their burrows in spring. The pale, blind, wingless workers stay behind, chewing wood.

A Blind World

The workers care for the eggs, carrying them out of the queen's chamber and lodging them in the maze of galleries. Every encounter with the queen is an occasion to stroke her with the antennae, and to groom her body. This is done between members of the colony whenever they meet, but the secretions of the queen make her especially attractive.

The vast majority of termites in any colony are blind, for in the absolute darkness of the nest, vision is useless. Termites communicate by constantly touching, and their senses of smell and touch are highly developed.

Food-sharing is one of the most common forms of tactile communication among termites. Partly digested food is passed to the queen and king, and some is given back. The food is passed around from the mouth or anus of one termite after another, until it makes the rounds of scores of individuals. This exchanging of food is called trophallaxis, and it serves to create and maintain social bonds, as well as to nourish.

Unlike the better-known termites that feed on wood, the *Macrotermes* eat fungus, grass, leaves, and plant litter. The fungus is grown in "gardens" at the base of the nest, fertilized with excrement. This is a frugal society that recycles everything.

The workers, which carry on construction with the help of nymphs, are the most numerous caste, but there are also many soldiers, sterile adult males and females that defend the nest. *Macrotermes* soldiers, which have large, armored heads and powerful mandibles that crush or pierce a foe, are so highly modified for their task that they cannot feed themselves and must depend on the workers for nourishment.

Another caste in *Macrotermes* society—and the only one to ever leave the nest—is the reproductive alate (meaning winged). Only a few nymphs develop into these specialized male and female forms. New colonies begin when the young alates swarm and take flight, which is usually in late summer for *Macrotermes*. Unlike other types of termites, alates can see and have a darker pigmentation, which protects them while outside.

After a short flight, the termites alight and shed their wings. The females perform a ritual dance and release a scent that attracts males. After a pair forms, they seek a suitable nest site and dig a cell into which they seal themselves. The first brood, a small one, must be cared for by the king and queen through several molts before the young are capable of taking over maintenance of the colony's needs. After a slow start, the colony gets under way, with the potential for becoming as large and complex as the nests from which the parents took flight.

Teeming Termite World

Social insects can accomplish large-scale construction feats that would be impossible for solitary insects. A *Macrotermes* nest may reach sixteen feet in height, sixteen feet across the base, and extend several feet into the ground. The cement-like walls, composed of soil particles hardened with saliva, are often two feet thick. They provide insulation against the fierce tropical sun, as well as an effective protection from invasion by ants and other enemies.

This self-contained world is a marvel of engineering skill. Special passageways built into the walls provide air conditioning. Warm, stale air from the labyrinth of crowded galleries rises to a hollow "attic" at the top of the nest. Here, heat is given off and the cooled air flows slowly down to the cellar through thin-walled ridges on the surface of the mound. As the air moves, it picks up oxygen from the outside. Workers constantly block off and reopen the air passages, apparently to regulate the microclimate of the nest. The large cell (lower right) is the queen's chamber.

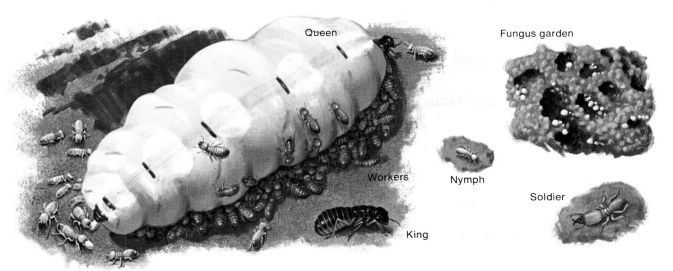

Queen

Fungus garden

Workers

Nymph

Soldier

King

The grotesquely swollen abdomen of a Macrotermes *queen is packed with eggs. Her size makes her a prisoner in her chamber, dependent on workers for food. Attracted by her scent, the workers feed and groom her constantly. A queen of this type may live as long as fifty years, and the* number of eggs laid in a lifetime is astronomical. The young hatch as nymphs, and begin work at once on chores ranging from fungus-farming to construction. If there is a shortage of soldiers, nymphs transform into soldiers. If a king dies, a male nymph develops into a new consort.

Umbrellas for
a downpour

Compass nests
of Australia

Skyscrapers
of Africa

A mountain
of "ashes"

Tropical termites are able to build year round, and some *construct architectural marvels. The tall chimneys that stand in crooked splendor on the savannas of Africa are generally made of red clay; their height aids ventilation. In rain forests, some termites build pagodas that resist* the thunderous downpours. The conical, ash-colored heaps of some species reflect the composition of the soil. In Australia, one species builds ten-foot nests, with the broad, flat sides facing east and west. These "compass" positions apparently help stabilize the temperature.

Some animals adapt to the dangers of their environment by forming small defensive groups. Others find safety in numbers

The adaptation of an animal to its environment is never a simple matter. To live in the icy seas, a seal doesn't just have thick fur: it has a bullet shape that allows it to swim well, a layer of fat that insulates, a great breathing capacity that helps it to stay underwater, and a host of other special physical and behavioral characteristics that enable it to survive.

Body and behavior are never separate, for in a sense, they are adapted to one another. In the deserts of North America, the tiny kangaroo rat holes up during the day, thus conserving the meager supply of water its body extracts from the seeds and grain on which it feeds. Its activity is nocturnal; its eyes are large, suited for seeing by the light of the moon and stars. The behavior of night feeding and the size of the eyes are interdependent adaptations to the conditions of the kangaroo rat's environment.

The beaks of birds are shaped by natural selection to suit the foods that are available; the teeth of grazing animals are flat to allow grinding, those of predators are sharp, enabling them to tear flesh. Whether chunky and slow or light and swift, nocturnal or diurnal, the animal is adjusted to its whole environment—not just to the land and climate, but to all other species present.

It would be strange if the structure of animal societies were not also influenced by the environment. But because social behavior is more elusive than physical structure or individual behavior, the case is harder to establish. We do not yet

The Beak Reveals a Way of Life

The study of one part of a bird's body, its beak, reveals not only what it eats but where it lives, and to some extent, how it behaves socially. A bird of prey, which needs a wide hunting area to find enough food, attacks competitors and is antisocial compared with other birds. At the other extreme, flamingos form large flocks, because the saltwater organisms on which they feed are usually present in abundance.

Seed cracker

Cardinals have tough beaks that enable them to crack seeds.

Pipette

A hummingbird's beak can reach nectar deep inside a flower.

Chisel

A woodpecker drills into the bark of a tree to find insects.

Knife

An eagle feeds on large prey. Its hooked beak tears flesh apart.

"Can opener"

An oystercatcher jabs its beak into a shell and pries it open.

Sifter

The flamingo's beak and tongue sieve food from "soupy" water.

know why tigers are solitary and lions social, or why some insects are social but the majority are not. There are advantages to both systems, but no easy explanations for the social structures we see.

A comparison of the social structures of two kinds of monkey—the yellow baboons of the African savanna and the hamadryas baboons of the dry Ethiopian brushlands—reveals that though these species are closely related, their social structures differ, each adapted to its own environment.

As the first light silvers the savanna, a group of yellow baboons begins to make its way down from high perches in the fever trees where it passed the night. By the time the sun is over the horizon, the entire group is on the ground.

This stand of trees is in the center of a twelve-square-mile area of east African grasslands, which constitutes the group's home range. During much of the year, a stream winds through the arching trees and provides drinking water. But now, in a time of drought, the stream bed is dust dry and the monkeys must travel to water.

An hour after sunrise, the group sets out on the day's business. It numbers forty-two individuals in all: two dominant males, five adult males of lower status, thirteen adult females, and twenty-two juveniles and infants of assorted ages. As they move out onto the savanna, the baboons fall into the defensive formation of their species: dominant males in the center; females with infants near the dominant males and other females; lower-ranking males spread around the perimeter.

The baboons travel roughly parallel to the dry stream bed, foraging as they go. Digging through the parched surface vegetation, they find succulent tubers and underground runners. Even in the dry season, the savanna provides enough food for these large ground-dwelling monkeys.

Under Attack

Midmorning, the group's leisurely foraging is abruptly halted by the excited warning barks of a young male at the edge of the group. The animals hastily close ranks and the dominant males rush out to meet the danger, an approaching trio of cheetahs. The confrontation is brief. A single baboon, separated from its fellows, would have made an easy meal for the cats, but an aggressive, aroused group is something else again. The cheetahs lope off in search of less formidable prey.

The baboons reach a tree-lined chain of water-holes by midafternoon. Ignoring the warthogs and impalas with which they share the water, the baboons drink their fill and move into the shade for

The savanna baboons of Africa live in the land of milk and honey. Food shortages are rare, and there are many places to hide. The baboons form large groups, with each member ready to sound the alarm at the approach of an enemy.

In the bleak area of North Africa where hamadryas baboons dwell, cover is scarce. Each evening, thousands of small harem families gather to sleep, perched on rocky ledges on the face of a cliff. Even in zoos, they prefer a stone bed.

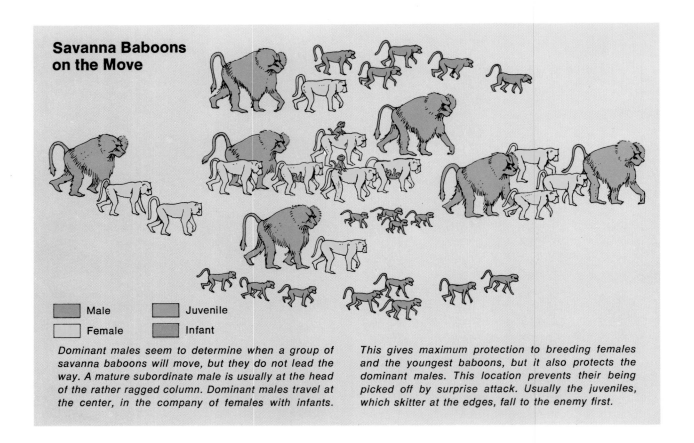

Savanna Baboons on the Move

Male | Juvenile
Female | Infant

Dominant males seem to determine when a group of savanna baboons will move, but they do not lead the way. A mature subordinate male is usually at the head of the rather ragged column. Dominant males travel at the center, in the company of females with infants.

This gives maximum protection to breeding females and the youngest baboons, but it also protects the dominant males. This location prevents their being picked off by surprise attack. Usually the juveniles, which skitter at the edges, fall to the enemy first.

a midday rest. Another baboon group is resting nearby. There is no mingling between the two groups, but neither is there strife; the drinking place falls within an overlap of home ranges, and the groups meet often during the dry season. Like human families at adjacent picnic tables, each simply minds its own business.

After a time, the dominant males set the group in motion across the savanna along a wide arc that brings them back to the fever trees before night. The journey is uneventful, except for a detour which keeps the monkeys downwind of a pride of lions. Baboons can face down most daytime predators with a show of strength, but lions are not easily intimidated.

Up a Tree

The sun is low when the group reaches its home stand of fever trees. A period of play, grooming, and general socializing rounds out the baboons' day. As the twilight deepens into dusk, the animals climb into their high sleeping perches and settle themselves for the night, relatively safe from attacks of such night hunters as the leopard.

The number of individuals in this society may

be anywhere from forty to eighty, and the events of the day may differ, but this social pattern is common to several species of savanna baboons (including the chacma and the olive) from the southern border of the Sahara to the Cape of Good Hope. Because food is abundant, the groups may grow to large size; there is enough for all even though many animals feed together. A large group is an advantage in defense in open country, which may offer little refuge.

An individual savanna baboon lives its whole life within the protection of its society, rising through the ranks from infancy to adult status, and perhaps to highest dominance. It cannot survive away from the others because it is easily picked off by predators, and it cannot readily join another group because savanna baboons attack strangers that approach too closely. Only occasionally will a stray be admitted to a group, and then only after it has endured much abuse.

North of the savanna, in the Ethiopian deserts and southern Arabia, living conditions and baboon social structure are both quite different. The country is rugged and food is scarce. Daily foraging for food is over a wider range, and fewer

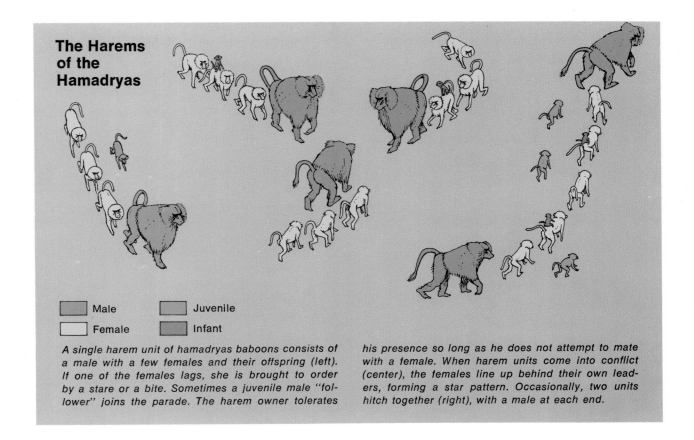

The Harems of the Hamadryas

Male
Female
Juvenile
Infant

A single harem unit of hamadryas baboons consists of a male with a few females and their offspring (left). If one of the females lags, she is brought to order by a stare or a bite. Sometimes a juvenile male "follower" joins the parade. The harem owner tolerates his presence so long as he does not attempt to mate with a female. When harem units come into conflict (center), the females line up behind their own leaders, forming a star pattern. Occasionally, two units hitch together (right), with a male at each end.

animals can feed in any one place. The existence of a large, protecting social organization is not possible under these conditions.

Instead of the defensive formation of savanna baboons, the basic social unit of the hamadryas baboon is a one-male harem made up of an adult male and one to four females and their young. The male is the sole protector of the group, and vigilant in keeping the harem by his side. If a female wanders away, she is quickly brought into line with a sharp bite on the neck.

Climbing Walls

All animals are vulnerable to predators when they sleep. No matter how strong the male—and in this species he is markedly larger than the female—his presence alone would not be sufficient protection at night. The hamadryas customarily climb down steep ravines or cliffs near riverbeds, gaining security from the inaccessibility of their sleeping perches.

As evening approaches, hundreds of harems converge on a single ravine, picking their way down the rock until the whole cliff is alive with chattering creatures settling down to sleep. Ac-

customed to tight formation, the harems remain together, and there does not seem to be any objection if several harems arrive that formerly used a different precipice.

Unlike the adult hamadryas females, which are constantly disciplined, juvenile and subadult males have considerable freedom of movement. They may attach themselves loosely to a harem, as "followers," trailing along to feed with the group. They are not driven away unless they attempt to mate with the females.

Upon approaching adulthood, a male starts his own harem by adopting a juvenile female out of a harem and carefully "mothering" her until she reaches sexual maturity. The possessiveness of the harem owner extends only to adult females, and the loss of a juvenile female—presumably his daughter—goes unchallenged.

The gelada baboon, which lives in nearby mountains, is not closely related to the hamadryas baboon (and, in fact, is not a true baboon), yet it has a similar social pattern. This suggests that the social structure is indeed influenced by the environment, for it has arisen in two different primate species under comparable conditions.

A paper wasp queen (left) prepares to lay an egg by inserting her abdomen into an empty cell. Eggs laid early in the season produce only workers. Future queens, which will found next year's colonies, hatch late in the summer.

A young adult paper wasp struggles out of its larval cell. Grublike larvae, which must be fed by workers or the queen, occupy several of the open cells. Cells with sealed tops contain larvae in the process of transforming into adults.

As a society passes its peak, provisions are made for a new generation to carry on

Societies tend to break up and renew themselves in regular patterns. The beginning of the breakup may come with the changing of seasons, or the society may simply become so large that forces binding its members lose their effectiveness.

Colonies of paper wasps living in the temperate zone begin to break up as autumn advances. Out of a colony of about 200 members, a few females will mate, then find sheltered nooks in which to hibernate. The other paper wasps perish.

The fertilized females emerge in spring and set about founding new colonies. When a female finds a suitable location, she begins constructing a paper-like nest from a mixture of plant fibers and saliva. One egg is laid in each cell; the offspring that hatch about fourteen days later will become the queen's first workers.

Several would-be paper wasp queens may begin work on the same nest. In the tropics, all construction usually stops when females encounter one another; they fight until only one is left alive. But in temperate regions, where the colony's growth is limited by the length of the summer, females of certain species may enter into an egg-eating contest instead of fighting to the death. At every opportunity, each female eats the eggs of her rivals and lays her own eggs in the empty cells. Eventually, one queen out-lays and out-eats the others, and the losers take up life as workers. The colony benefits in two ways: its labor force is increased and the cells built by the losers are used by the winning queen. The colony thus grows more rapidly than it would if the losers died.

Through the spring and most of the summer, all the offspring develop into female workers. But as the season passes, males are produced, and also a caste of non-worker females, sometimes called "foundress daughters." These are the future queens. They are fed by the workers and accumulate food reserves for their period of hibernation. The males receive little care; their survival through the winter is not necessary for the perpetuation of the species.

By the end of the summer, the tempo of activity in the hive has slowed almost to a standstill. No new cells are constructed, and the queen stops laying eggs. As the food supply dwindles, the adults may even cannibalize the remaining young.

Finally the nest is abandoned. Foundress daughters mate with the males and go into hibernation. The next spring the survivors renew the colony.

Among birds, too, the coming of cold weather often heralds a drastic change in the social order. Instead of forming bonded groups in which each individual has a definite relationship with at least a few others, the birds join in huge aggregations. All individuals in such groups are more or less anonymous—almost like fish in schools.

Many songbirds, such as goldfinches, chaffinches, and pipits, abandon the territories they so staunchly defended throughout the spring and summer, and gather peaceably in winter flocks. The social structure is built anew the following spring, when territories are claimed and mates courted. In these species, individuals do not seem to seek out the same mate or nest of the previous year, though they may return to the same woods.

Life in a Gaggle

The greylag goose, on the other hand, stays with the same mate year after year. This European goose is the ancestor of all domestic geese. In the wild, the family unit is the pair, as it is among almost all geese and swans.

Entry into adult greylag society begins in the winter juvenile flock. The young males and females mill around, and from time to time a pair will go through the "triumph ceremony" of the greylag. They run forward with outstretched necks and raised wings, calling loudly. This seems a quaint way of making friends, but for the geese it is a strong declaration of interest.

At first the young birds just "flirt" and "date" for a while within the adolescent flock. Later they begin to "go steady." This is the progression toward true courtship leading to pairing. Though greylags are generally paired for life, there are occasional "divorces." Once pairs are formed, the daily triumphing reinforces the pair bond.

When the breeding season arrives, youngsters that have paired in the winter flock join in the competition with old established pairs for a nesting site and territory in the long rushes beside a lake. Pairs that are not successful in claiming a suitable site do not breed. They remain together, but must wait a year before rearing a family.

Families stay together as a gaggle until late summer, when the parents lead their young into a flock made up of many families. Here, the young begin a new social life, flying to nearby meadows to graze, or to quiet streams to crop the lush herbage. They familiarize themselves with the countryside around and develop relationships with other greylag families in the flock. Soon they enter a juvenile flock and pairing begins, bringing the greylag pattern to full cycle.

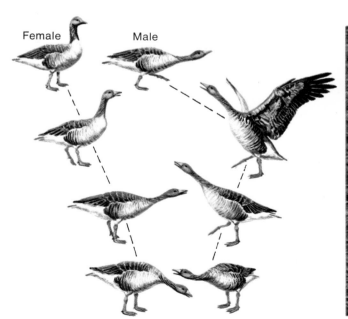

A greylag goose triumph ceremony begins as a male, trumpeting loudly with his head thrust out, advances on a real or imagined enemy. Then the male returns to his partner and the two stand together cackling in each other's ears.

A gaggle of geese consisting of a greylag goose and gander and their offspring swim sedately on Norfolk Broads in England. In the spring the parents will raise a new brood, and the young birds will join a juvenile flock.

For Asian water buffalo, wallowing is a necessity. In regions near the equator, they suffer extreme discomfort unless able to soak during the heat of the day. If drought should strike a region where they live, high mortality is inevitable.

Disaster and Privation

Most social changes are annual, but natural disasters can also cause the splitting of societies. Each year the size of a female herd of water buffalo increases with the arrival of new calves. From time to time the monsoon rains come late. Edible vegetation becomes sparse and most of the water holes dry up. Weakened by long walks to water from distant pastures, nursing females — their strength drained by their calves — converge on the few existing water holes. These become wallows of thick, sticky mud, and the buffalos often do not have the strength to struggle out. Hundreds die in a single creek bed, packed together like cattle in a stock pen.

Small groups become scattered across the countryside, and when the next monsoons arrive the survivors begin to build family herds. Each of the units will continue to grow until the next drought decimates their numbers.

In good times or bad, a pride of lions is a loose organization, its composition constantly changing as new litters of cubs arrive, as young males reach maturity and depart to wander on their own until they can form a pride, and as aging leaders are defeated by younger males.

The size of the pride largely depends on the availability of prey animals. In times of plenty it may include twenty or thirty members. But in leaner times, starvation and disease can reduce the pride, or some members may drift away in a wider search for food.

Membership in a pride confers only limited security, but the flexibility of the structure and its capacity for renewal bestow important advantages on the species as a whole.

Lion cubs begin life without the protection of the group; the female leaves the pride to give birth. The first few weeks are precarious for the cubs because the mother must divide her time between hunting for herself and feeding them. In her absence, the helpless cubs are easy prey if found by hyenas, leopards, or other lions. Handicapped because she must hunt alone, the lioness may not find enough food to sustain herself and the litter, and she may abandon her offspring.

A well-fed pride of lions *that settled under the shade of a tree continue their nap, even though the shadow has moved. Such a picture of contentment is evidence of good hunting. In hard times, prides are smaller and individuals are leaner.*

When the cubs are about two and a half months old, their mother introduces them to the pride, and life becomes a bit more secure. The mother now shares the kills of other pride members, and while she hunts, "baby-sitters" are usually available for the cubs.

A Precarious Infancy

A typical pride might consist of two adult males, six females, and a dozen or so young of assorted ages. A harsh reality of lion life is thrust on the cubs almost at once: although the entire pride displays tolerance, and even affection, for them, at mealtime they are at the bottom of the social order. When a kill is made, the males eat first, followed by the females and juveniles. Only when the others have finished are the cubs allowed to eat. The cubs often go hungry, and in lean times many starve. Not more than half the lion cubs born survive to maturity.

At about six months, the cubs begin to follow the adults on the hunt. At first they are worse than useless. Lions rely upon patient, stealthy stalking to get within charging distance of their prey. The blundering, inexperienced cubs spoil many a stalk. Still, their presence is tolerated. Only by such practice can they gain the necessary skills. Not until they are about a year old do cubs master the hunting technique well enough to be of some use to the pride.

When male lions reach three years of age, they are driven away by the dominant males. The young bachelors, which sometimes form an all-male group, now have the problem of establishing prides of their own. To do so, they must either affiliate themselves with unattached females or, more commonly, depose the dominant male of an existing pride—at the risk of their lives.

A pride is often led by two males. The truce between them may be an uneasy one and subject to sudden breach, but as long as it is maintained, the lions' united efforts can turn away a single would-be usurper. When such partnerships break down, the stronger of the two drives out the weaker. In turn, the winner is eventually driven off by one or two strong young bachelors.

A queen honeybee (marked with blue paint) makes her way slowly across a comb, laying eggs as she goes. She is so specialized for reproduction that she could not found a new colony without the help of her retinue of workers.

After leaving the old hive, a queen and her swarm of workers often settle temporarily in the branches of a tree or shrub. Scouts then take off from the seething mass in search of a suitable place in which to build a new hive.

The Upper Limits

The size of a pride fluctuates in response to food supply and the struggles of individual animals. But there are other societies, such as that of the honeybee, that split in two when they exceed their maximum number.

A single queen honeybee controls the activities of tens of thousands of workers by means of substances secreted by her salivary glands and perhaps by other glands. This "queen scent" is licked from her body by the workers attending her, and spread throughout the whole community by contact between individuals.

When a hive grows extremely large, the queen's scent may no longer reach members at the periphery even if she remains alive and active. The isolated bees then behave as if the queen had died; a "replacement" queen is produced, and a portion of the colony's population, bonded to this new leader by her scent, establishes a separate hive.

In other bonded groups, monkeys for example, recognition between members is predominantly by sight, rather than by scent. In such species, the maximum size of a society is limited to some extent by the memories of individual animals.

Apparently, no monkey troop can grow indefinitely. The group structure of savanna baboons becomes unstable when it passes a certain size. An aggregation of 103 was seen to split occasionally during the day into two groups of sixty-six and thirty-seven, each with a proportional distribution of dominant males, adult females, subordinate males, and juveniles. Though they foraged separately, the two bands would reunite in a single group in the evening. This seems to be the first step in the formation of new groups. Two other groups—of fifty-one and sixty-six individuals— were often observed close to each other, arriving at the same water hole at the same time and occupying adjacent sleeping trees. It seems likely that these animals once formed a single society, and that the division had become nearly complete.

A band of Japanese macaques studied by scientists was given unlimited supplies of food at an observation station. At the beginning of the study, the troop numbered about 220 members. Six dominant males were near the center, surrounded by females and infants. Around this core lived the subordinate males and ten mature males of "subleader" status. The six central males exerted social controls; they broke up fights among the females and dominated the ten subleaders at the periphery. These ten, in turn, controlled disruptions among the masses of low-ranked males.

A mob of macaques in a Japanese forest, part of a group of 200, gives an impression of chaos. But each macaque has its place, and leaders keep inferiors where they belong. If a group gets too big, policing breaks down and the group splits.

A State of Disorder

Under the artificial condition of plenty, the monkeys produced a population explosion. In six years, the troop grew from 220 members to 580 — a size probably never attained naturally. The six dominant males and their ten lieutenants were hard put to keep order in the jumble of quarreling subordinates.

With the general lessening of central control, the monkeys at the edges of the troop reacted in much the same way as honeybees at the periphery of an extremely large hive. A new leader arose and, joined by five other young males, formed the nucleus of a new troop. Females drifted from the center of the main troop to join the "revolutionaries," and in time the splinter group recruited about seventy members. The secession was both peaceful and gradual; ten months elapsed be-

tween the time the troop showed the first signs of splitting and the time the new troop had taken on a definite identity of its own.

Human protection and feeding of the monkeys fostered further population growth, and soon afterward the main troop split again. Now three troops lived where one had reigned. Although both splits occurred under somewhat unnatural conditions, it seems likely that wild troops of Japanese macaques divide in a similar way.

Factors other than population growth can lead to splitting. In a troop of about 160 Japanese macaques, an old male was demoted from third in dominance to fourth. When usurped further by a subleader, the old male abruptly defected from the troop, taking about forty of its members with him. Thus in some species, the "personality" of an individual may affect the social equation.

A dying elephant cow, trunk limp and body shrunken, stands apart (left) from the herd. They watch anxiously, and a bull comes to her side, sniffing and making gentle rumbling noises, urging her to join them. Moments later, she collapses.

Screaming and trumpeting, the herd hastens to the side of the fallen cow. The bull shoves others aside and tries to raise her, pushing with forehead and tusks, but she is too heavy. He forces grass into her mouth. All the frantic efforts fail.

Requiem for an Elephant

Few animals live surrounded by comrades that are ready to give aid. Fewer still die with attendants at their deathbed. Perhaps it is because elephants are so long-lived — African elephants have been known to live for seventy years — that their ties are so strong. The death throes of one produce not just distress in its herdmates, but a frenzy of shrieks and the kind of helpless fury that is sometimes seen in hospitals when a bereaved human being is suddenly confronted with death. These elephants in the Serengeti National Park in Kenya express concern and grief to an extent seldom seen among animals.

In a gentle salute, the bull lays his trunk on the body of the dead cow. Throughout the afternoon, he tries repeatedly to rouse her, as the herd feeds restlessly nearby. One by one, the family units—each led by a large cow—return to the body to trumpet and sniff. Finally, in the late afternoon, the herd shuffles away, as a calf lingers by the body.

A Glimpse of Time

A human lifetime is but a moment in the evolution of life on this planet. No one lives long enough to see the workings of evolution in a grand scale. But the process of natural selection goes on. A million years from now, some creatures will be much as they are today, others will be drastically changed, and still others will be extinct.

The process of evolution is by its very nature gradual. Some changes, it is true, do take place in a remarkably short time; a species of British moth has, within about a hundred and fifty years, switched from light pigmentation to dark, as pollution of the environment increased. The dark moths survived best against the soot-stained trees. Recently, with abatement of pollution the moths seem to be reverting to a light coloration.

But after all, it was only the color of the moths that changed noticeably. Throughout their "quick-change" act, the insects remained physically the same in other ways.

The changes man is making in the environment often happen too fast for the evolutionary process to work for the survival of animals. What defense can a polar bear possibly develop when it is relentlessly pursued by a hunter in a helicopter? It can only run until it drops of exhaustion. If an osprey consumes pesticide-laden fish, and the chemicals cause the bird's eggs to be too thin-shelled to bear its weight, there is no evolutionary remedy, no natural way for the species to cope with this sudden disorder.

No one knows how the extinction of polar bears or ospreys might ultimately affect other species—or, indeed, how many animals are affected when even a small thicket is cleared away at the edge of a garden. Scientists have only just begun to study animal interrelationships—how the tiger affects the deer; and how wolves and moose coexist, prey and predator, in a kind of rough balance.

The natural world is complex beyond the calculation of computers. What we don't know about the ways of animals may interfere with what we are ever able to find out—for we may do irreparable damage from sheer ignorance. The safest means of keeping the earth green and populated with animals is for man to tread lightly.

In the long history of animal evolution, the rise of families and the development of social bonds were events that profoundly changed the quality of animal life. Membership in a herd entitles any elephant to the protection and solici-

A mother harp seal rears up on her flippers in a threat posture beside her week-old whitecoated pup. Harp seals are born on ice floes in the North Atlantic and Arctic oceans in late winter. The pups weigh about twenty pounds at birth, but within two weeks grow to nearly 100 pounds on the mother's rich, creamy milk. When fur hunters come, a terrified mother may remain beside her pup, but she is powerless to save it. Though the Canadian government has recently put restrictions on the slaughter of whitecoats, it will probably take strictly enforced international regulations to save these gentle animals from extinction.

tude of all. Injured or ill, the individual has friends. Other members of the herd will crowd around and attempt to give whatever aid they can, trumpeting their alarm at the plight of a distressed fellow elephant.

Musk oxen, too, have social ties that seem almost heroic. They will not leave an injured herdmate as long as it is still alive. This behavior serves the musk oxen well in dealing with their chief natural enemies, wolves. But such attachments have caused many a herd to be wiped out by human hunters, for one stricken member holds the others there, making them all an easy target.

It is a cruel irony that such marvelous social adaptations should work to the disadvantage of animals. It would be a far better thing to preserve the natural world, so that animals may live out their remarkable lives, and human beings may —for as long as our species survives—watch and enjoy them. Probably what will save animals at this crucial hour is not the love that some people have for a few species, or the wish to learn from them, but something stronger: a feeling of respect, which is the human bond to animals.

Bibliography

and recommended reading

The publishers wish to acknowledge their indebtedness to the following books and periodicals, which were consulted for reference or as sources of illustration. The field of animal behavior is fascinating and fast-moving. We hope that reading *Animal Families* will encourage readers to delve further into this amazing world, and follow its progress in the periodicals recommended. Publications of particular interest to the general reader are marked with an asterisk (*).

ALLEE, WARDER C., and others, *Principles of Animal Ecology*. Saunders, 1949

* ALLEN, ARTHUR A., and others, *Stalking Birds with Color Camera*. National Geographic, 1963

* ALLEN, DURWARD L., *Our Wildlife Legacy*. Funk & Wagnalls, 1962

* *Animals You Will Never Forget*. Reader's Digest, 1969

* AUSTIN, OLIVER L., JR., edited by HERBERT S. ZIM, *Song Birds of the World*. Golden Press, 1967

BARNETT, SAMUEL A., *Instinct and Intelligence: Behavior in Animals and Men*. Prentice-Hall, 1967

* BASTOCK, MARGARET, *Courtship: An Ethological Study*. Aldine, 1967

* *Book of British Birds*. Drive Publications, London, 1969

* BOURLIERE, FRANCOIS, *The Natural History of Mammals*. Knopf, 1964

* BROWN, LESLIE, *Africa: A Natural History*. Random House, 1965

* BROWN, LESLIE, and DEAN AMADON, *Eagles, Hawks and Falcons of the World*. McGraw-Hill, 1968

CARTHY, J. D., and F. H. EBLING, editors, *The Natural History of Aggression*, Academic Press, 1965

CLOUDSLEY-THOMPSON, J. L., *Rhythmic Activity in Animal Physiology and Behavior*. Academic Press, 1961

* COSTELLO, DAVID F., *The World of the Porcupine*. Lippincott, 1966

CRANDALL, LEE S., *The Management of Wild Mammals in Captivity*. University of Chicago Press, 1964

* DARLING, F. FRASER, *A Herd of Red Deer: A Study in Animal Behaviour*. Oxford University Press, 1937

DE VORE, IRVEN, editor, *Primate Behavior: Field Studies of Monkeys and Apes*. Holt, Rinehart & Winston, 1965

ETKIN, WILLIAM, editor, *Social Behavior and Organization Among Vertebrates*. University of Chicago Press, 1964

* EVANS, HOWARD ENSIGN, *Wasp Farm*. Natural History Press, 1963

* EWER, R. F., *Ethology of Mammals*. Plenum Press, 1968

* *Fascinating World of Animals*. Reader's Digest, 1971

* FISHER, JAMES, and ROGER TORY PETERSON, *The World of Birds*. Doubleday, 1968

FORBUSH, EDWARD HOWE, and JOHN RICHARD MAY, *A Natural History of American Birds of Eastern and Central North America*. Houghton Mifflin, 1955

GILLIARD, E. THOMAS, *Birds of Paradise and Bower Birds*. Natural History Press, 1969

* GILLIARD, E. THOMAS, *Living Birds of the World*. Doubleday, 1958

* GOODALL, BARONESS JANE VAN LAWICK, *My Friends, the Wild Chimpanzees*. National Geographic, 1967

* GRIFFIN, DONALD R., *Bird Migration*. Doubleday, 1964

* GROSSMAN, MARY LOUISE, and JOHN HAMLET, *Birds of Prey of the World*. Clarkson N. Potter, 1964

HAFEZ, E. S., editor, *The Behavior of Domestic Animals*. Williams & Wilkins, 1969

* HEDIGER, HENI, *The Psychology and Behavior of Animals in Zoos and Circuses*. Dover, 1969

* HEDIGER, HENI, *Wild Animals in Captivity*. Dover, 1964

* HILL, ROBIN, *Australian Birds*. Funk & Wagnalls, 1968

HINDE, ROBERT A., *Animal Behavior: A Synthesis of Ethology and Comparative Psychology*. McGraw-Hill, 1966

* HUTCHINS, ROSS E., *Insects*. Prentice-Hall, 1966

* HUXLEY, JULIAN S., *Courtship Habits of the Great Crested Grebe*. Grossman, 1968

JAY, PHYLLIS C., editor, *Primates: Studies in Adaptation and Variability*. Holt, Rinehart & Winston, 1968

* JEWELL, P. A., and CAROLINE LOIZOS, editors, *Play, Exploration and Territory in Mammals*. Academic Press, 1966

* JOHNSGARD, PAUL A., *Waterfowl: Their Biology and Natural History*. University of Nebraska Press, 1968

JOLLY, ALISON, *Lemur Behavior: A Madagascar Field Study*. University of Chicago Press, 1966

KLOPFER, PETER H., *Behavioral Aspects of Ecology*. Prentice-Hall, 1962

KUMMER, HANS, *Social Organization of Hamadryas Baboons*. University of Chicago Press, 1968

LACK, DAVID, *Ecological Adaptations for Breeding in Birds*. Methuen, London, 1968

* LACK, DAVID, *The Life of the Robin*. Witherby, London, 1965

* LARSON, PEGGY PICKERING, and MERVIN W. LARSON, *Lives of Social Insects*. World, 1968

* LORENZ, KONRAD Z., *King Solomon's Ring*. Crowell, 1952

* LORENZ, KONRAD Z., *On Aggression*. Harcourt, Brace & Jovanovich, 1966

LORENZ, KONRAD Z., *Studies in Animal and Human Behavior*. Harvard University Press, 1969

MANNING, AUBREY, *An Introduction to Animal Behavior*. Addison-Wesley, 1968

MARLER, PETER, and WILLIAM J. HAMILTON III. *Mechanisms of Animal Behavior*. Wiley, 1966

* *Marvels and Mysteries of the Animal World*. Reader's Digest, 1964

* MECH, L. DAVID, *The Wolf: The Ecology and Behavior of an Endangered Species*. Natural History Press, 1970

MORRIS, DESMOND, *Primate Ethology*. Aldine, 1967

* NELSON, BRYAN, *Galapagos: Islands of Birds*. Morrow, 1968

ORR, ROBERT T., *Animals in Migration*. Macmillan, 1970

* *Our Amazing World of Nature*. Reader's Digest, 1969

PALMER, RALPH D., editor, *Handbook of North American Birds*, Vol. I. Yale University Press, 1962

* PETERSON, ROGER TORY, *Field Guide to Western Birds*. Houghton Mifflin, 1961

PETTINGILL, OLIN SEWALL, JR., *Ornithology in Laboratory and Field*. Burgess, 1970

RAND, AUSTIN L., *Ornithology: An Introduction*. Norton, 1967

* RHEINGOLD, HARRIET L., editor, *Maternal Behavior in Mammals*. Wiley, 1963

* RUE, LEONARD LEE, III, *The World of the Beaver*. Lippincott, 1964

* SANDERSON, IVAN T., *Living Mammals of the World*. Doubleday, 1961

SCHALLER, GEORGE B., *The Deer and the Tiger: A Study of Wildlife in India*. University of Chicago Press, 1967

* SCHEFFER, VICTOR B., *The Year of the Seal*. Scribner's, 1970

* SCHEFFER, VICTOR B., *The Year of the Whale*. Scribner's, 1969

* SMITH, L. H., *The Lyrebird*. Lansdowne Press, Melbourne, 1968

SMITH, ROBERT L., *Ecology and Field Biology*. Harper & Row, 1966

SNOW, D. W., editor, *Proceedings of the XIV International Ornithological Congress*. Blackwell Scientific Publications, Oxford, 1967

* SPARKS, JOHN, and TONY SOPER, *Penguins*. Taplinger, 1967, 1968

THOMSON, A. LANDSBOROUGH, editor, *A New Dictionary of Birds*. McGraw-Hill, 1964

* TINBERGEN, NIKOLAAS, *Social Behaviour in Animals*. Methuen, 1965

* TINBERGEN, NIKOLAAS, and HUGH FALKUS, *Signals for Survival*. Clarendon Press, 1970

WALKER, ERNEST P., and others, *Mammals of the World*. Johns Hopkins Press, 1968

* WELTY, JOEL CARL, *The Life of Birds*. Saunders, 1962

Periodicals

Animal Behaviour, London

* *Animal Kingdom*, New York

* *Audubon*, New York

Behaviour, Leiden, Holland

BioScience, Washington, D.C.

Birds of the World, London

* *International Wildlife*, Milwaukee, Wisc.

* *National Geographic*, Washington, D.C.

* *National Wildlife*, Milwaukee, Wisc.

* *Natural History*, New York

* *Naturalist*, Minneapolis, Minn.

Nature, London

New Scientist and Science Journal, London

* *Purnell's Encyclopedia of Animal Life*, London

Science, Washington, D.C.

* *Scientific American*, New York

* *Smithsonian*, Washington, D.C.

Index

Page numbers in bold type refer to illustrations

Index

Page numbers in bold type refer to illustrations

Index

Page numbers in bold type refer to illustrations

Index

Page numbers in bold type refer to illustrations

Picture Credits

Frontispiece: Michael C. T. Smith / National Audubon Society. 6 Allan Roberts. 8 L. David Mech. 9 Denys Ovenden. 10 (top left) N. Smythe; (top right) E. R. Degginger; (bottom) Allan Roberts. 11 Bill Dugan. 12 (left) Dee Jay Nelson / National Audubon Society; (right) Robert W. Mitchell. 13 Anne Brewster. 14 Steve Wilson / DPI. 15 (left) Kellner Associates; (right) Nick Drahos. 16 Sy Barlowe. 17 (left) Graham Pizzey; (right) Peter Slater / Photo Researchers. 19 (top) Jean B. Thorpe; (bottom) Brian Hawkes / National Audubon Society. 20 (top) Allan Roberts; (bottom) Kellner Associates. 21 (top left) Alan Root; (top right) Thase Daniel; (bottom) Leonard Lee Rue III / National Audubon Society. 23 Leonard Lee Rue III. 24 (top) Kenneth W. Fink; (bottom) Anne Brewster. 25 Kellner Associates. 26 Lancelot Tickell. 27 Michael C. T. Smith. 28 Patricia Caulfield. 29 Thase Daniel. 30 Burney J. Le Boeuf. 31 (top) Nick Drahos; (bottom) Kellner Associates (after Rheingold). 32–33 Jen & Des Bartlett. 34 Jane Burton / Bruce Coleman Inc. 36 Floyd Norgaard / Lenstours. 37 Larry West / Full Moon Studio. 38 George Kelvin (after DeVore). 39 Kellner Associates. 40 (maps) George Kelvin; (top right) Thase Daniel. 42 P. P. de Moor. 43 (left) Kellner Associates (after Walther); (right) Erwin A. Bauer. 44 Norman Myers. 45 René P. Bille. 46 Kellner Associates (Steller's jays, after Brown; zebra finches, after Morris; wolves, after Schenkel; gulls and oystercatchers, after Tinbergen). 47 Kellner Associates (cats, after Leyhausen; elephants, after Kühme). 48 T. W. Hall. 49 (left) George Kelvin (after Carpenter); (right) Hladik / Jacana. 50 (top) Jane Overman; (bottom) George Kelvin (after Hediger). 51 Quentin Keynes. 52 (top) John S. Crawford; (bottom left) Norman Myers; (bottom right) Cyril Toker / Frederic Lewis. 53 (top left) John S. Crawford; (top right) Kellner Associates; (bottom) Ingeborg Lippman. 54 Kenneth W. Fink. 55 Kellner Associates (after Mykytowycz). 56 Erwin A. Bauer. 57 Kellner Associates (after McBride). 58 Kellner Associates. 59 E. R. Degginger. 60 (top left) George Kelvin (after Nero); (top right and bottom) Thase Daniel. 61 G. C. Kelley. 62 Charles Fracé. 63 (left) Kenneth W. Fink; (right) Charles Fracé. 64 (top) Rod Allin; (bottom) Norman Myers. 65 Norman Myers. 66 Norman Myers / Bruce Coleman Inc. 68 L. H. Smith. 69 (top) Harry Engels; (bottom) Kellner Associates. 70 Harry McNaught (from "The Reproductive Behavior of Ring Doves," by Daniel Lehrman, © November, 1964, by Scientific American, Inc. All rights reserved). 71 Thase Daniel. 72 Norman Myers. 73 N. Smythe. 74 Kenneth W. Fink. 75 George Kelvin. 76–77 Harry McNaught. 79 Myron E. Scott. 79 (left) Masood Quarishy / Bruce Coleman Inc.; (right) Erwin A. Bauer. 80 Kellner Associates. 81 William J. Bolte. 82 (top) Graham Pizzey; (bottom) Kellner Associates. 83 Jane Overman. 84 (top) Ed Park; (bottom) Wilford L. Miller. 85 (top) Alan Root; (bottom) Leonard Lee Rue III. 86 (top) Thase Daniel; (bottom) Kellner Associates. 87 (top left) Graham Pizzey; (bottom left) Bill Ratcliffe; (right) Jack Dermid. 88 Eric Hosking. 89 (left) George Kelvin; (right) Michael J. Ursin. 90 (top) Norman Chaffer; (bottom) Kellner Associates. 91 Harry McNaught. 92 (top) Kenneth W. Fink; (bottom) Eric Hosking. 93 (left) Jim Anderson; (right) George Kelvin. 94 Alan Root. 95 Burney J. Le Boeuf. 96 Norman Lightfoot. 98 (top) William D. Griffin; (bottom)

Edward Malsberg. 99 (left) André Fatras; (right) William H. Stribling. 100 (left) William D. Griffin; (right) Edward Malsberg. 101 (top) G. R. Roberts; (bottom) Sy Barlowe. 102 (left) M. F. Soper; (right) Edward Malsberg. 103 Norman Chaffer. 104 Norman Myers. 106 Marineland of Florida. 107 Tom Myers. 109 (top left) Helen Cruickshank; (top right) Jack Dermid; (bottom left) Edward Malsberg; (bottom right) William D. Griffin. 110 Caulion Singletary. 111 Harry McNaught. 112 (top) Jen & Des Bartlett; (bottom) Sy Barlowe. 113 Jen & Des Bartlett. 114 Edward Malsberg (after McBride). 115 Allan Roberts. 116 (top) Norman Myers / Bruce Coleman Inc.; (bottom) E. S. Ross. 117 Harold J. Pollock. 118 Stan & Kay Breeden. 119 Sy Barlowe. 120 (left) Alan Root; (right) Kellner Associates. 121 (top) E. S. Ross; (bottom) William D. Griffin. 122 Jen & Des Bartlett. 123 (top) E. R. Degginger; (bottom) Jane Overman. 124 (left) G. R. Roberts; (right) Norman Myers. 125 Charles Fracé (after Rheingold). 126 (top) Sy Barlowe; (left) Jean B. Thorpe; (right) Dennis Brokaw / National Audubon Society. 127 (top) André Fatras; (bottom) Alan Root/Okapia. 128 Jane Overman. 129 M. Philip Kahl. 130 Rod Allin. 132 James A. Kern. 133 Edward Malsberg (after M. W. Fox). 134 Jean B. Thorpe. 135 Jen & Des Bartlett. 136 (left) Jane Overman; (right) Olive Glasgow. 137 (top) Nick Drahos; (bottom) Leonard Lee Rue III. 138 Durward Allen. 139 Edward Malsberg (after Walther). 140 Wilford L. Miller / Phil Starkle. 141 Mark N. Boulton / Bruce Coleman Inc. 142–143 Harry McNaught (after Altmann). 144 George Laycock. 145 (top) John Kaufmann; (bottom) Ingeborg Lippman. 146 Thase Daniel. 147 (top) Kenneth W. Fink; (bottom) Harry McNaught. 148 (top) Helen Cruickshank; (bottom) Anthony Mercieca. 149 Charles Fracé (after McBride). 150 (top) Ned Smith; (bottom) Charles Fracé. 151 (left) William J. Cromie; (right) Kellner Associates. 152 (top) Caulion Singletary; (bottom) Leonard Lee Rue III. 153 (top) Leonard Lee Rue III; (bottom left) Charles Fracé; (bottom right) Ned Smith. 154 Norman Myers / Bruce Coleman Inc. 155 (top) E. S. Ross; (bottom) Rod Allin. 156 Nick Drahos. 157 (top) Karl H. Maslowski; (bottom) G. C. Kelley. 158 (top) Norman Myers; (bottom) Jean B. Thorpe. 159 (left) Tom McHugh / Photo Researchers; (right) Edward Malsberg (after Curry-Lindahl). 160 John Warham. 162 Charles Fracé. 163 John Carnemolla. 164–165 Alan Root. 166 (top) Grant Haist; (bottom) Bill Dugan (after Lorenz). 167 Leonard Lee Rue III. 168 E. S. Ross. 169 Nick Drahos. 170–171 Robert Kray. 172 Edward Malsberg. 173 (top) Leonard Lee Rue III; (bottom) Russ Kinne / Photo Researchers. 174 Edward Malsberg (after DeVore). 175 Edward Malsberg (after Kummer). 176 Grace A. Thompson / National Audubon Society. 177 (left) Charles Fracé (after Lorenz); (right) Eric Hosking / Bruce Coleman Inc. 178 George Holton / Photo Researchers. 179 Alan Root. 180 (top) Tom Myers; (bottom) Treat Davidson / National Audubon Society. 181 T. Iwago / Photo Trends. 182 Horst Munzig / Susan Griggs. 183 (top) Horst Munzig / *Life* Magazine © Time, Inc.; (bottom) Horst Munzig / Susan Griggs. 184–185 Fred Bruemmer.

Photo Editor: Robert J. Woodward